Vermuyden and the Fens

A Study of Sir Cornelius Vermuyden and the Great Level

SIR CORNELIUS VERMUYDEN

Supposed contemporary portrait attributed to VAN MIEREVELD (1567–1641), in Author's possession.
(see Appendix, page 159.)

Vermuyden and the Fens

A Study of
Sir Cornelius Vermuyden
and the Great Level

By
L. E. HARRIS

With a Portrait of Vermuyden
and other Illustrations
from contemporary sources

London
Cleaver-Hume Press Ltd

Cleaver-Hume Press Ltd
42a South Audley Street
London, W.1

First published 1953

PRINTED IN GREAT BRITAIN
BY WESTERN PRINTING SERVICES LTD., BRISTOL

CONTENTS

LIST OF ILLUSTRATIONS

Details of sources are given on each plate. The Author's thanks for permission to reproduce are due to the Cambridge Antiquarian Society and Messrs. Bowes and Bowes Ltd. in respect of the Frontispiece and Plates I–V; Mr. A. Hollestelle and Messrs. J. M. C. Pot of Tholen, Holland, in respect of Plate II; and the Great Ouse River Board in respect of Plates V and VI.

FOREWORD

WHILE this book is the result of many years of labour and research on my part, it could never have been written without the assistance of the many friends to whose help it is now my pleasant task to pay a heartfelt, but quite inadequate, tribute. From the many who have contributed so much it is difficult to single out any to whom more acknowledgement is due than to others, but if I have to make this unenviable choice, the names which spring to my mind are those of Lt.-Col. Maurice Noel and Mrs. Noel. By their generous gift to me of the contemporary portrait of Sir Cornelius Vermuyden, which I have reproduced in the book, they have inspired in me an even greater interest in that unusual man than I already possessed, and confirmed my half-formed determination to write a book about him, a book which, I hoped, might destroy some long-standing misconceptions about his work in the Great Level of the Fens, and give to him some of the credit too long withheld.

Of my many friends connected with the River Boards of this country, and with the difficult task of Fen Drainage, my thanks are specially due to Mr. W. E. Doran, O.B.E., Chief Engineer of the Great Ouse River Board, Cambridge, for placing at my disposal the Proceedings of the Bedford Level Adventurers, and other of the invaluable documents in the Fen Office at Ely, on which so much of this book is based; to Mr. E. L. Kelting, O.B.E., Chief Engineer of the Somerset River Board, if only for his inspiring interest in bibliography, and in the story of Sedgmoor, and to Mr. G. McLeod, late Chief Engineer to the Middle Level Commissioners, for allowing me to examine the documents in the possession of the Commissioners. Professor Bruce Dickins of Cambridge University has given me much assistance in a variety of ways, and I am indebted for help to Mr. H. H. Foster, Clerk to the Malvern Conservators, to Mr. E. H. Sargeant, County Archivist, Worcester, to Mr. F. N. Fisher and Miss Nellie Kirkham of Derby, both of whom are making a special study of Vermuyden's connection with the Wirksworth Lead Mine, and especially to Dr. D. P. Lambert of Giggleswick who has borne with my enthusiasm for so many years, even to the extent of wading through, and criticising helpfully, one of the early typescripts of this book. My thanks are also due to Miss P. W. Shield for her expert searching of records which has contributed so much to the enlightenment of the story.

And finally I come to my friends in Holland. Of Dr. Johan van Veen, Chief Engineer, Rijkswaterstaat, I can only say that his is, perhaps, the greatest debt which I have to repay. His own wide knowledge of, and love for, the past history of land drainage and reclamation has been proved by his own book *Dredge, Drain, Reclaim*, but in spite of this he has been more than patient with my absorption in my own small self-allotted field. He has widened my knowledge, by showing me something of his country, and particularly the province of Zeeland and the town of St. Maartensdijk, the birthplace of Vermuyden. From Mr. P. Jaspersee, the 'opzichter' of St. Maartensdijk, I have gratefully received so much information of that town in which he has such a specialised interest. And to Dr. Fockema Andreae of Leiden I express my gratitude for so many helpful suggestions, for the hard work which he has done on my behalf, for his friendship, and for the assistance which I have derived from his own historical writings.

L. E. Harris

Histon, Cambridge,
April 1953

INTRODUCTION

THE period of and around the middle years of the seventeenth century has provided material for many an individual biographical study. It is, perhaps, the period in English history in which for the first time in the popular imagination of modern times, the characters become beings of flesh and blood instead of cardboard figures with names. The tragedy of King Charles, the loyalties and sometimes chivalries of the Civil War, the romanticised political abilities of men like Pym and Hampden, the autocracy of Oliver Cromwell, all build up to a picture of history which, even if sometimes distorted, remains in our minds from youthful days as a tale of real people. It was in that period that the best of Cornelius Vermuyden's work was done, and on that account, perhaps, it was his misfortune to be somewhat overshadowed by the events of the Civil War itself and by the strange evolution back to the sanity of the Restoration through the Commonwealth and Protectorate. Partly for that reason the true realisation of the quality and value of his work is a development only of modern times after he has for nearly three centuries been denied his true recognition.

The materials for a personal history of a man do not lie only in the professional activities and accomplishments of the individual. Something more is needed, perhaps the written testimony of contemporaries, or of the individual himself. In the case of Sir Cornelius Vermuyden nothing of this nature, or practically nothing, has survived, if indeed it ever existed. For some thirty-five years extending over the reigns of two sovereigns and over part of the Commonwealth and Protectorate he occupied a position of undeniable, if varying, importance, and during that time he was closely associated with the two kings, James and Charles, and with Cromwell himself, to say nothing of Francis and William, Earls and first Duke of Bedford. During this period he must have come into contact with numerous other individuals in Court and Parliamentary circles and yet, apart from scattered references in State Papers, or in a few private communications, all concerning his work or intended work, maybe in Malvern Chase, the lead mines of Derbyshire, in Yorkshire, or in the Great Level of the Fens, there is little on which we can build up a picture of Vermuyden the man.

It may be that we at the present time, at least in a comparatively limited circle, credit more importance to Vermuyden's work in the Great Level than was the case in the seventeenth century. On the other hand it is doubted whether in general there is yet adequate appreciation of the value of his achievements to our present economic existence, or of the fact that the drainage of the Great Level of the Fens is a piece of social history of which the results are now being seen in their true light.

In the popular mind, and the serious historian has never given him more than scant attention, Vermuyden is usually known, where he is known at all, as the man who drained the Fens, but, of course, the Vermuyden story is not quite so simple and straightforward as that, while the statement is to a certain extent inaccurate because his work in the Fens was confined to the Great Level, or Bedford Level as we know it today, comprising only about 307,000 acres, or something less than half the total Fenland area of over 700,000 acres. It is not suggested that this detracts in any way from the greatness of Vermuyden's achievement but it does provide an example of the looseness of thinking associated with the man if, indeed, much thought has ever been devoted to him. Almost up to the present day it has been customary to base a judgement on him not on an independent evaluation of the available evidence but on what has been said before. Thus the adverse criticisms of the seventeenth century have been slavishly followed and repeated in the eighteenth and nineteenth, and even in the twentieth, centuries until today a happily more enlightened, and hence more charitable, judgement has been reached based on a wider knowledge of the principles of land reclamation, of hydrology generally, and of the particular problems of the Fenland.

Samuel Smiles in the nineteenth century, in his *Lives of the Engineers*, made some attempt to write a life of Sir Cornelius Vermuyden but in the absence of any real personal details was compelled to rely almost entirely on the works rather than the man to make the story. Korthals-Altes[1] in the twentieth century wrote a book entitled *Sir Cornelius Vermuyden* to which he mistakenly added the sub-title 'The Lifework of a Great Anglo-Dutchman', but in this he dealt almost exclusively with Vermuyden's work in Hatfield Chase, Yorkshire, and disposed of his work in the Great Level, by far the bigger undertaking and extending over a much longer period of his life, in two or three pages. And so both these books fail to achieve their professed aims if their titles are to be taken seriously. In spite of which, however, they are useful contributions to the story of Vermuyden if only for the reason that they both show some appreciation of the value and magnitude of his achieve-

[1] J. KORTHALS-ALTES, *Sir Cornelius Vermuyden*. London and The Hague, 1925.

ments, in spite of the inaccuracies of which they, and particularly Korthals-Altes, are often guilty.

This present book is not intended to be a history of the draining of the Fens. That need has been more than adequately filled by Dr. Darby's valuable work[1] to which every historian of any phase of that history must be indebted. What the present book sets out to do mainly is to present a critical assessment of Vermuyden's work, an assessment based primarily on that work in the Great Level, on a new interpretation of contemporary records, and on the use of some contemporary records which have hitherto been neglected.

Although, as has been said above, the Great Level to which Vermuyden's work in the Fens was confined covers less than half the whole Fenland, it was undoubtedly owing to the lead which he gave there that the eventual recovery of the whole 700,000 acres, and its conversion from swamp to fertile agricultural land, became a practical reality. Thus, on that reasoning alone, Vermuyden is important and his story worth telling, although it must be appreciated that he was in no way responsible for the desire, the urge, to drain the Fens. He was merely the agent through whom that desire, which had long been in existence, was translated into positive action. There is no denying, however, that that action was to a large extent resultant upon the determination of Vermuyden himself.

If Vermuyden had the misfortune to be overshadowed by events he was in one respect fortunate. When he came to England in or about the year 1621 he came from the Isle of Tholen in the Province of Zeeland where the art of land reclamation was a tradition, and he arrived in England at a time when the accumulation of seemingly isolated incidents had led to a real interest in the possibilities of Fen drainage. Indeed a more opportune moment for his arrival could hardly have been chosen. Chance may have played some part in the choice but it is more reasonable to conclude that, as will be apparent from what is said in a later section of this book, there was conscious design on the part of certain shrewd and hard-headed Netherlanders which determined when the young Vermuyden should seek his fortune, and theirs, in England.

The drainage of the Great Level of the Fens was not, as has been said earlier, the only work which Vermuyden accomplished, but it was certainly the largest and the one on which the judgement of his capabilities must fundamentally be based. Furthermore, it is the one phase in his career most fully documented and, therefore, of outstanding value to the historian. The invaluable collection of documents in the Fen Office at Ely, while it covers

[1] H. C. Darby, *The Draining of the Fens.* Cambridge, 1944.

a period far beyond the known life of Vermuyden, contains the original Proceedings of the Bedford Level Corporation from the year 1649 onwards. A critical examination of those Proceedings forms a large part of this book, and they provide an insight into the difficulties with which the Corporation was faced in its initial years. But what is more, they enable some evaluation to be made of the character of Vermuyden and if that evaluation is totally different to that arrived at by Samuel Wells in 1830[1]—and we shall examine his comments at a later stage—the divergence is due, it is hoped, to a more unbiased examination than Wells thought that, by the nature of his employment, he was justified in making. In addition, the developments of the past one hundred and twenty years provide a wider and truer background against which to pose the criticism.

It should be emphasised that during the last two hundred years or so there has been a regrettable, successive, and unquestioning acceptance of so-called facts in connection with the life and work of Vermuyden, a phase which has been so well, or shall we say so unfairly, exemplified by the writings of Samuel Wells himself, and which has resulted in the discrediting of Vermuyden. To paraphrase a statement of Fox-Davies on the study of Armory,[2] 'some statement appears in a book about Vermuyden, it is copied into book after book, and accepted by those who study Vermuyden as being correct, while all the time it is absolutely wrong'. Thus the adverse criticisms of the seventeenth century, the unsubstantiated 'facts' of this and succeeding centuries, were repeated so that, starting with the vindictive pamphlets of Andrewes Burrell of 1641—we shall hear more of this gentleman later in this book—there has been an uninterrupted progression of vilification until the judgement of to-day.

Vermuyden was no paragon of virtue and no attempt will be made to show that he was. His was a complex personality, but whatever his faults, he possessed the qualities of foresight, determination, and energy in no small degree. His achievements, and Vermuyden himself, are worthy of a wider recognition, and, in addition, a wider justice than at present prevails. He starts in uncertainty and ends in comparative obscurity. In between lie thirty-five years and his work at Dagenham, Hatfield Chase, and in the Great Level. The last of these provides the surest foundation on which to base a reasoned judgement of what must be admitted as his greatness, the evidence for which, it is hoped, will emerge from the pages of this book which, while it deals with other aspects of Vermuyden's career, must primarily be a story of 'Sir Cornelius Vermuyden and the Great Level of the Fens'.

[1] S. Wells, *History of the Bedford Level*, 1830.

[2] A. C. Fox Davies, *A Complete Guide to Heraldry*, 1929.

CHAPTER ONE

Early history of Fen drainage. Influence of the Fenland Abbeys, and effects of their dissolution. Rise of the Russell family. Their Fenland estates.

THE Fen country, that flat expanse of fertile land which lies on the east of England, is bounded on the seaward side by the North Sea and the wide indentation of the Wash, and inland by the high ground of the counties of Lincolnshire, Northamptonshire, Cambridgeshire, Suffolk and Norfolk. Through this plain wander the slow rivers, the Witham, The Welland, the Nene and the Ouse, and many centuries ago as they meandered with flat gradients to their outfalls in the Wash, there were times when they were unable to carry away through these partially closed and choked outfalls the water coming from the highlands, with the result that the rivers over-spilled their natural banks and flooded the surrounding country. Thus were created the waterlogged, fenny and marshy wastes, providing little more than a sanctuary for wildfowl, and the breeding place for fish and eels, incapable of bearing crops other than rushes and sedge. Here and there perhaps a small patch of high ground on which human habitation had been created where the 'breedlings', as they were termed, pastured their meagre flocks above the marsh water and lived precariously by trapping eels and wildfowl. As William Camden[1] wrote at the beginning of the seventeenth century, 'They that inhabit the fennish country . . . were even in the Saxon times called Girvij, that is, as some interpret it, Fen-men or Fen-dwellers. A kind of people according to the nature of the place where they dwell, rude, uncivil, and envious to all others whom they call upland-men, who stalking on stilts, apply their minds to grazing, fishing, and fowling. The whole region itself, which in winter season and sometimes most part of the yeare, is overflowed by the spreading water of the rivers Ouse, Grant, Nen, Welland and Witham, having not loades, and sewers large enough to voide away.'

[1] WILLIAM CAMDEN, *Britain, a Chorographical Description of the most flourishing Kingdoms of England, Scotland and Ireland*, 1610.

That was the picture which the Fens presented at the opening of the seventeenth century, and yet before the close of that century hundreds of thousands of acres of land which from time immemorial had been abandoned to the wildfowl, to the reeds and the sedge, had been reclaimed and drained of the stagnant waters to form, as they do today, some of the richest agricultural land in the kingdom. The Fenland today provides roughly three-quarters of a million acres of land unsurpassed in productivity anywhere in these Isles, and thus it is no exaggeration to say that the draining and reclamation of the Fens represents a permanent and important influence on the social and economic history of England. The story with which this book is concerned is that of Sir Cornelius Vermuyden and the seventeenth century. The very early history of the Fens has little bearing on that story, but it will be, perhaps, of interest to relate something of the events which in the years before 1630 contributed to the vital decision of that year to 'lay dry' the Great Level. Quite clearly this was not a sudden and unpremeditated decision. It had a background, and this in itself was the background to Vermuyden's work. Thus it should be understood.

While it is true that the draining of the Fens is a seventeenth-century story, indeed, to limit it more closely, it can with justice be termed a Stuart story, it would be wrong to imagine that no attempts had been made in earlier centuries to reclaim some of the marshy land. Such attempts, however, were only of a piecemeal nature. The true reclamation had to wait until the seventeenth century because, firstly, there was until then no adequate appreciation of the need for a drainage scheme of wide scope, and, secondly, the capital necessary for such a scheme was not available. Whether the Romans drained the Fens during their occupation of Britain is a debatable question. There are certainly indications that they cultivated the Fens, and there are finds of Roman relics to show that the Romans lived there. There is the evidence of aerial photography to show that at one time there existed in the Fens a system of agriculture earlier than, and different from, that of the Anglo-Saxons and, therefore, presumably Roman. There are traces still remaining of a channel named Car Dyke skirting the high ground on the inland boundary of the Lincolnshire Fens, eventually joining the River Ouse at Waterbeach, near Cambridge. It has been suggested that the Car Dyke was built by the Romans as a catchwater drain to form part of their comprehensive system of drainage in the Fens, but there is no direct evidence to support this suggestion, and the more reasonable conclusion is that the Car Dyke was a navigational channel[1] and that there was no

[1] Sir Cyril Fox, *The Archaeology of the Cambridge Region*, 1923. See also Gordon Fowler, *Proc. Camb. Ant. Soc.*, Vol. XXIII, pp. 117–124, 1933.

general Roman system of drainage for the reason that, the land surface being higher than it now is, the natural drainage system then sufficed. In later centuries the land surface became lower, the rivers with their flat gradients and choked outfalls flooded over their banks to create the Fenland as our seventeenth-century ancestors knew it.

But all this is largely surmise and while the later mediaeval history of the Fens can be, and has been, examined,[1] to say when the draining of the Fens began is like trying to define something which until the year 1630 was merely nebulous and indeterminate. Perhaps the first attempts to drain portions of the Fens came from the Fenland abbeys which grew out of the simple religious foundations of the seventh and eighth centuries—the abbeys of Ramsey, Crowland, Denny, Soham, and the cathedral church of Ely for example—owning as they did large tracts of Fenland and from these raising a large proportion of their ample revenues. But in the true meaning of Fen reclamation the abbeys contributed very little. The final dissolution of the monasteries and religious houses generally in the reign of Henry VIII, and the transfer of their extensive properties to the Crown was completed in the year 1540. Naturally the change of ownership of the lands in the possession of the Fenland abbeys must have influenced the course of the history of Fen reclamation in the seventeenth century—and the story of Vermuyden. On the other hand, there is little to show that by the transference of that ownership an intelligent and co-ordinated drainage system was destroyed, and the story that the drainage of the Fens suffered a disastrous set-back by the dissolution of the monasteries is really one of those easy generalisations which have slipped into history without much inquiry.

Undoubtedly the monastic establishments had concerned themselves with some form of primitive and elementary drainage works in the Fen lands in their possession, but it is on record that 'before the death of Edward I, the central government had been called in to oversee and supplement the local drainage arrangements, and, from 1294 onwards, commissions under the royal seal were appointed one after another at short intervals'.[2] And then in 1339, 'the King being informed that the banks, ditches, and sewers at Wysebeche, Elme, and Welle, were broken, and out of repair, issued a commission . . . to enquire thereof; and through whose default they became so ruinous; and who were the land-holders thereabouts, or had safeguard by the said banks; and to distrain them for their repair, according to the proportion of their lands.'[3] Admittedly these particular lands were not in the

[1] H. C. Darby, *The Mediaeval Fenland*, 1940.

[2] Victoria County History, *Huntingdonshire*, Vol. III, p. 256.

[3] W. Dugdale, *History of Imbanking and Draining*, 2nd ed. 1772, p. 306.

immediate neighbourhood, nor, possibly, the direct concern, of any abbey, but there is plenty of evidence in subsequent years of many royal commissions relating to lands in various other parts of the Fens which tend to prove how widespread was the interest of the Crown in, and its jurisdiction over, the preservation of works of drainage, whether banks or drains. In other words, for some hundreds of years before the dissolution of the religious houses the Crown was taking an active interest in the protection of the Fens, and thus there is no reason to suppose that, after 1540, there was any tendency on the part of the Crown to abandon this interest in the lands outside the possession of the dissolved houses, or to fail to extend its control over the lands which passed from the abbeys to the Crown. It has been rightly stated that 'to the abbeys and the see of Ely, though they did but little to improve the region, the Fens were of the utmost importance in their natural state. Actually, this usefulness may account, in part, for the fact that the ecclesiastical landowners showed no ambition to attempt any large-scale project of drainage.'[1] That being the case, it would be illogical to suggest that if, as seems clear, the state of the Fens did deteriorate subsequent to the dissolution, this deterioration was due to the removal of a control exercised by the abbeys over the drainage. Certainly there was the isolated example of the work of Bishop Morton, in the fifteenth century, and his attempt to improve the course, and hence the drainage capacity, of the River Nene by the making of the straight cut from Stanground near Peterborough to Guyhirne some six miles upstream of Wisbech. This work, still to this day called 'Morton's Leam', was a praiseworthy attempt to extend the scope of the drainage scheme, but it fell far short of being a co-ordinated and comprehensive project embracing the whole Fenland, which, experience in later centuries was to prove, was the only remedy of any value.

Even if, at the time of the dissolution, the abbeys did possess 'all the faults of corporate bodies which had outlived the work for which they had been created'[2] it would be hard to characterise the act of dissolution as ethically justified, a consideration with which, however, we are not concerned here. The sole interest to us of the dissolution lies in the influence which it had on the draining of the Fens. The seizure of the lands of the religious houses by the Crown merely involved the substitution of the Crown as landlord in place of those houses—and the abbeys were landlords only to the tenants of the lands—and dealing with the Fenland abbeys in particular, if that state of affairs had continued it might have resulted in eventual benefit to the drainage since the replacement of many landlords by one, the

[1] VICTORIA COUNTY HISTORY, *Huntingdonshire*, Vol. III, p. 258.
[2] F. A. HIBBERT, *The Dissolution of the Monasteries*, 1910.

Crown, might in turn have led to some scheme of drainage embracing all the Fenland as one unit. Unfortunately this was not to be the case. The primary purpose of the dissolution was the enrichment of the Royal Treasury, whatever high-principled motives may have been publicly advanced, and once the monastic lands were in the hands of the Crown they were quickly disposed of, some granted as rewards for faithful service, most sold for cash.

Thus it will be seen that, far from the ideal of one landlord for a large portion of the Fenland being realised, what in fact resulted was a further multiplication of landlords, and, consequently, of the interests involved in the drainage. Needless to say, this change resulted in no advance towards a complete co-ordination of interest but, because there never had existed during the life of the abbeys any co-ordinated system of drainage, it is certain that the effects of the change were not so harmful as has sometimes been believed. The Crown still exercised its well-intentioned, but somewhat piecemeal, control over the state of the drainage, and still appointed its Royal Commissions, but many years were to elapse before there would come a realisation that the salvation of the Fens lay in a comprehensive, all-embracing scheme of drainage. The importance of this point cannot be over-emphasised. If, as will be shown later, Humphrey Bradley in 1593 was the first to make proposals for a scheme for draining the Fens as a whole, or for the major part of the Fens, this principle of a comprehensive scheme was one to the importance of which Cornelius Vermuyden was fully alive from the moment when he began his long connection with the Great Level, and to uphold his convictions on this point he had to struggle very hard. Proof of this will emerge as our later story unfolds. But if the dissolution exercised little adverse effect on the drainage of the Fens, it certainly had an influence on the history of that drainage, and on the whole a favourable one.

When, in the year 1550, John Russell, one of a line of prosperous West Country merchants, was created first earl of Bedford by Henry VIII, he had already, from his first employment under the Crown of Henry VII, served three successive monarchs with distinction. He owned extensive property in the West Country and 'with the earldom came a fresh grant of land including manors in Devon and Cornwall which had been part of the possessions of the attainted Marquess of Exeter . . . and finally a grant from monastic lands which was the house and part of the property which had belonged to Thorney Abbey in Cambridgeshire.'[1]

John Russell, 1st Earl of Bedford, probably had a poor opinion of these lands in the Fens, mainly waterlogged as they may have been, certainly in comparison with his richer holdings in the West. It is not suggested, how-

[1] GLADYS SCOTT THOMSON, *Two Centuries of Family History*, 1930.

ever, that this was the reason why he settled the lands of Thorney, together with the estate of Thornhaugh in Buckinghamshire, on his fourth and youngest son William. Nor could he have foreseen the vital influence that this settlement was to have on the draining of the Fens. Now William in due time served his Queen, Elizabeth, in the wars in the Netherlands. He had been Governor of Flushing and had been knighted for his services, and was eventually created Baron Russell of Thornhaugh. When in the Netherlands he had seen the work which the Dutch were doing in the draining and reclamation of their flat land from the flood waters of the rivers and from the incursions of the sea. Sir William, as he then was, had the intelligence to draw a parallel between the Netherlands and his own Fenland estate of Thorney to which he had succeeded on the death of his father. In the year 1590 when, as we shall see, there was an awakened interest in the reclamation of 'drowned' lands, he took the positive step of bringing three Dutchmen over to England, Jan Petersen, Jan Jacobson and Waris Alart, to examine the Fens of Thorney and to report on the possibility of draining them, but while documents still survive in the archives of the Russell family at Woburn giving details of the Dutchmen's visit, no written report giving their conclusions has come to light. It appears, indeed, doubtful if one was ever made. One item of the scrupulous accounts covering the expenses of the Dutchmen's visit which do survive in the Woburn records details an expenditure of two shillings 'for a guide which brought the strangers to Northall for to speak with Sir William' when, presumably, they told him verbally what their conclusions were. They must have reported that the draining of the fens in Sir William's possession was a feasible and profitable proposition because some time later Sir William addressed a request to the Privy Council asking that he might be permitted to drain these lands with the aid of Dutch settlers for whom he prayed for certain privileges to be granted—freedom from impressment, exemption from subsidies, and so on.[1]

The reply of the Privy Council was generally favourable to these requests but there the matter ended, and, presumably, Sir William lost interest, for no documents exist to show that anything further was done. The whole project was, of course, of minor extent, and it is doubtful if the original conception embraced more than, say, some 2,000 acres, whatever it might have subsequently grown to, but if for the time being the Thorney fens remained undrained and undisturbed, the incident has some considerable significance because Sir William's son, Francis, eventually became 4th Earl of Bedford on the death of his cousin Edward, the 3rd Earl, and, of course, inherited the Thorney estates on his father's death. Francis headed the band of 'adven-

[1] GLADYS SCOTT THOMSON, *Family Background*, 1949.

turers' who, under the Lynn Law, of 1630 and the Indenture of Fourteen Parts, as we shall see later, engaged Cornelius Vermuyden to carry out the drainage of the Great Level, the first, and final, comprehensive scheme of drainage in the Fens which stands there today fundamentally unchanged.

It is not too much to conclude that the decision of Francis to engage in this 'adventure' must have been influenced by the knowledge of what his father had contemplated in 1590. It is equally maintainable that if the dissolution of the monasteries had not occurred in 1540, and if, therefore, the Thorney estates had not passed into the possession of the Russell family, the course of the history of the draining of the Fens might have been very different from what in fact it became. It is not suggested that, if there had been no dissolution of the monasteries, and if, therefore, the Thorney estates had remained in the possession of the abbey, there would never have been a co-ordinated scheme for the drainage and reclamation of the Fens. The inference, however, is that in all probability the initiation of such a scheme would have been long delayed.

CHAPTER TWO

Developments under Elizabeth I and James I. Vermuyden's birth. The Vermuyden and Liens families in Zeeland. General Drainage Act of 1585 and proposals of Humphrey Bradley. Sir Clement Edmonds' report of 1618.

ALL through the later years of the reign of Queen Elizabeth there was in England a widespread interest in the possibilities of the reclamation of the Fens, both on the part of private individuals and of the Crown. This interest, to a certain extent, owed its origin to the work of land reclamation seen in the Netherlands during the fighting there in which so many Englishmen had taken part, and to the close connection existing between the two countries at that time. The economy of the Netherlands demanded the utmost employment of all lands in the country, but at first sight it is somewhat difficult to appreciate the motives from which sprang the intention to reclaim flooded lands in England in the sixteenth and seventeenth centuries. The country was far from being over-populated, and far from being fully exploited agriculturally. Why, then, should the financially hazardous operation of Fen drainage be undertaken? The answer lies in one word, money, or to be more explicit, while the Crown may have looked with one eye on the draining of the Fens as a means of increasing the agricultural productivity, and thus, as we should say today, of raising to some extent the standard of living, the other eye was fixed firmly on the financial gain which would accrue to the Treasury. In the year 1585 an Act had been introduced into the Commons entitled 'An Act for the recovery and inning of drowned and surrounded grounds and the draining dry of watery marshes, fens, bogs, moors and other grounds of like nature'. This Act, as its title implies, was not confined to the Fenland itself but was intended to embrace all 'drowned and surrounded grounds' throughout the kingdom. Sixteen years were to pass before, in 1600, it reached the Statute Book but the intentions expressed in the Act give a clear indication of the attitude of the Crown to the whole subject of land reclamation.

Whatever may have been the intentions of the Crown, and the motives behind them, as far as the private individual was concerned, his interest was manifestly and solely monetary gain, and the reclamation of 'drowned and surrounded grounds' was to him merely a financial speculation. But there was at that time in England little, if any, experience of the form of co-operative undertaking for an enterprise of this nature by means of which so much of the land reclamation in the Netherlands had been financed, and finance was, of course, the one imperative need without which no project could prosper. A scheme for the draining and reclamation of the Fens proper as a whole, an all embracing and comprehensive scheme which, as must be emphasised again, alone could be of real effectiveness, called for finance on a grand scale, a scale far beyond the resources of a single individual, and certainly beyond those of an impoverished Treasury. In the Netherlands the co-operative scheme of land reclamation, the 'onderneming', was a commonplace by the end of the sixteenth century,[1] and it is not surprising, therefore, that the lead in England came from a Netherlander. In 1593 Humphrey Bradley, of Bergen-op-Zoom, a Brabanter of English descent, submitted to Lord Burghley a project for draining the Fens of Norfolk, Suffolk, Lincolnshire, Cambridgeshire, Northamptonshire and Huntingdonshire, claiming that he could accomplish the task with the labour of 700 to 800 men at a cost of £5,000, and that the greater part of the work could be accomplished in six months time. He estimated that the annual benefit to the Crown would be £40,000, and he told Lord Burghley that if neither he nor the King was prepared to entertain the proposition, he, Bradley, would 'bring the name of certain gentlemen of wealth who were willing to perform it, upon reasonable conditions.'[2]

For the time being we must leave Bradley's propositions to later discussion because at, or about, the date when these were presented, the sphere of interest of our present story shifts from England to the Netherlands. In the year 1590 a son was born to Sara, wife of Gillis Vermuyden, a prosperous and respected citizen of the town of St. Maartensdijk, in the isle of Tholen, of the Province of Zeeland. That son was later to become Sir Cornelius Vermuyden.

Now it is true, as we have said above, that the economy of the Netherlands demanded the employment of every acre of land, but, indeed, the need for artificial means of embanking and draining was even more pressing than demanded by economic considerations. On the efforts of a large proportion of the inhabitants in the construction of embankments and drains depended the very survival of the land itself. Holland as we know it today

[1] S. J. Fockema Andreae, *Waterschaporganisatie in Nederland en in den Vreemde.* Amsterdam, 1951.
[2] *Cal. State Papers Dom. Eliz.* CCXXIV. 97.

consists largely of the delta portions of two rivers, the Maas and the Rhine, while the province of Zeeland can be considered as a portion of these two deltas combined with deltaic material brought down by the River Schelde. Many thousands of years ago the North Sea between the Netherlands and England did not exist, the two countries were joined together and England formed part of the continent of Europe, while the River Thames was a tributary of the Rhine. Later on, when the cleavage had occurred, and the deltas of the three continental rivers were building up, a row of sand dunes formed along the whole of the west coast of the Netherlands, protecting the delta lands from the North Sea, but while these dunes persisted, and still exist, along the coast of the province of Holland, in Zeeland breaches occurred, the sea swept in, and what had been continuous delta land became the series of isolated islands, Walcheren, Schouwen, Noord-Beveland, Tholen, and so on, which we know today. It must, however, be emphasised that these islands in the form which we know them now are in many cases largely the result of the efforts of the inhabitants in reclaiming, or 'impoldering' this precarious land from the ravages of the water. All this will give some idea of the tradition of land reclamation which stretched behind the Zeelanders in the seventeenth century, and from as far back as the tenth century the Low-German potentates, the Bishops of Bremen, the counts of Holstein and Lubeck, and others, employed the coastal Dutch for the reclamation of swamps and flooded lands in their territories.[1]

At the beginning of the seventeenth century the family of Vermuyden had been long established in the town of St. Maartensdijk and was evidently of some substance. As early as the year 1315 the name of Colaird van der Muden appears in a charter connected with the dykes of the Muijerpolder in the jurisdiction of the town, while twenty-four years later, in 1339, the name again appears in connection with the Middelland polder. Eventually the name became Vermuye, and later Vermuyden, although as late as 1570 we find that one of the aldermen of St. Maartensdijk was described as Bartel van der Mue, but alternatively known as Bartel Marinuss Vermuyden, or Vermuyen.[2] This worthy gentleman, a grandfather of Sir Cornelius Vermuyden. lived to the ripe old age of 84 years and now lies beneath a stone slab in the church with the inscription:

> HIER LIET BEGRAVEN BARTEL M. VERMUYEN GEWEEST BORGHM^{R} DESER STEDE STERF A^{O}1609 DEN APRIL OUDT 84 JAHREN.

[1] BERNARD H. M. VLEKKE, *Evolution of the Dutch Nation*, New York, 1945.

[2] A. HOLLESTELLE, *Geschied en Waterstaatkundige beschrijving van de Waterschappen en Polders in Het Eiland Tholen.* Tholen, 1919.

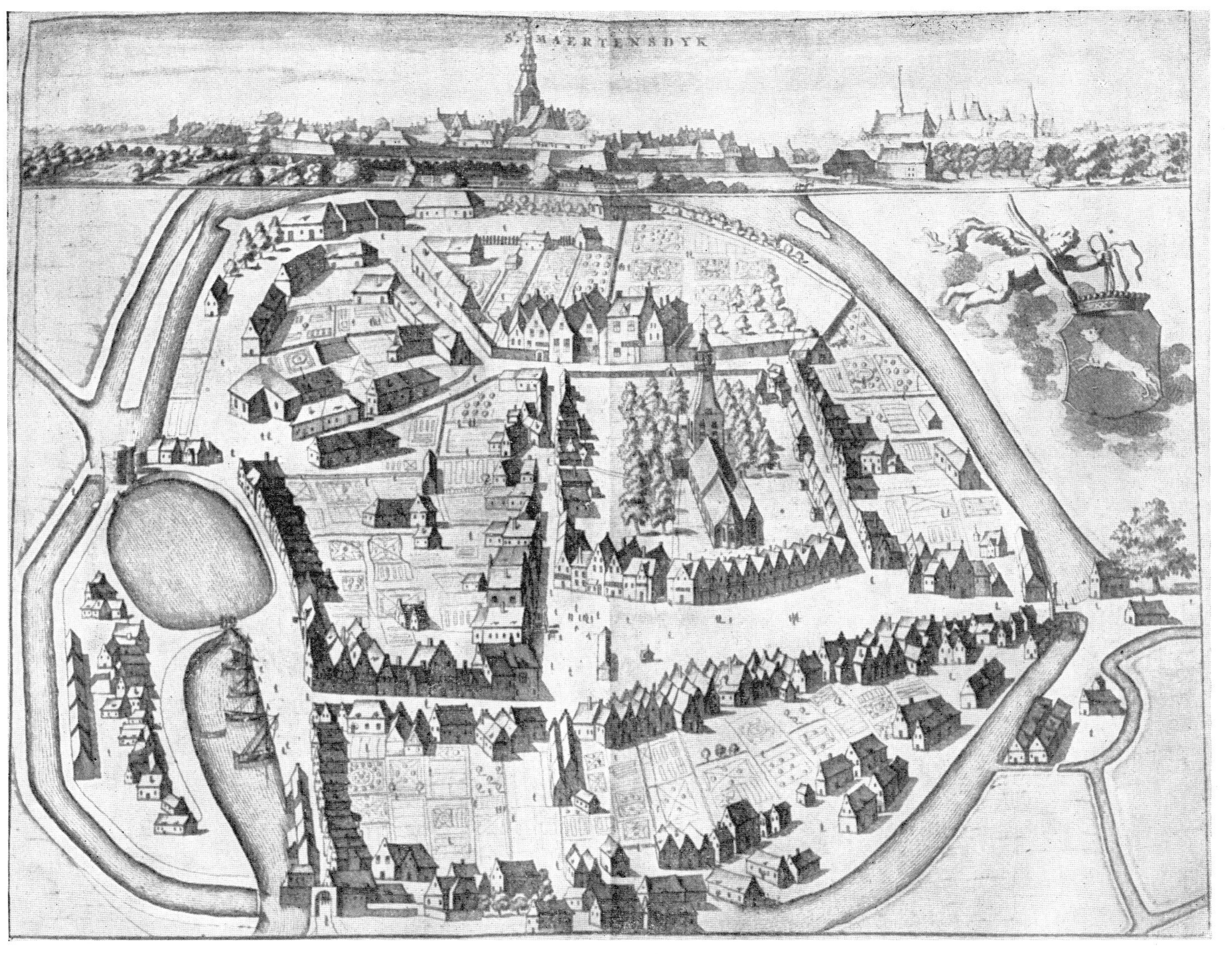

PLATE I. Plan of the Town of St. Maartensdijk in 1689.
From A. Smallegange, *Nieuwe Cronijk van Zeeland*, Middleburg, 1696.

Of comparable, if not greater, importance in St. Maartensdijk at the time of which we are writing was the family of Liens, and while it has not been possible to find a reference to this family as far back as 1339, the year when Colaird van der Muden appears, certainly they were conspicuous in the early sixteenth century in matters of administration connected with polder reclamation. In 1580 a Jacob Liens is mentioned in relation to the Hikkepolder of Oud-Vossemer on the north-east side of the Isle of Tholen, and today there is on the front wall of the little seventeenth-century town-hall in the market square of St. Maartensdijk a tablet commemorating the fact that Cornelius Liens was a member of the town council in the year 1628. It is of interest to note also that in the archives of St. Maartensdijk[1] there is the record of a contract made on 4 October, 1614, by the town council with Pieter Hendericksss, a clockmaker of Bergen-op-Zoom, for the building of a new town clock, similar to the one which he had already made for the town of Arnemuiden, for the sum of 316 Flemish pounds, 13 schillings, 4 groates, and in this record are given details of the sums which were to be contributed towards the cost by various prominent citizens. This list is headed by the name of the 'rentmeester' Joachim Liens for the sum of 8 pounds, 6 schillings, 8 groates, the two burgomasters 3 pounds each, the aldermen 2 pounds each, and so on down to the minister and schoolmaster for one pound each. Then follow particulars of others who will contribute for the provision of bells in the church, Johannes Liens the 4th bell, Cornelius Vermuyden and his brother the 5th bell, Phillipus Liens the 3rd bell, Hendrik Liens the 2nd bell, and others.

All this gives a picture of the stability, the importance of the Vermuyden and Liens families and, as will be seen later, the latter family was to have a very vital influence on the career of Cornelius Vermuyden in England, an influence exercised primarily by Joachim Liens, the 'rentmeester', and his brother Cornelius, the town councillor. Now this influence was far from being entirely fortuitous. There would clearly be a close identity of interests between the families of Vermuyden and Liens in a small community such as that of St. Maartensdijk. Cornelius Vermuyden's mother, Sarah Werckendet before her marriage to Gillis, was one of a family of some prominence in the town of Zierikzee, the capital of the neighbouring Isle of Schouwen, and her brother, Burgomaster Lieven Werckendet, had been prominent in the work of embanking and impoldering in the island, and in the construction of the harbour of Zierikzee. The close connection between the two families had been further emphasised by Sarah's marriage, since the mother of Joachim and Cornelius Liens had been Phillipine Werckendet, a great-

[1] *Archief St. Maartensdijk*, Nr, 1, fol. 49, 51, 52.

aunt of Sarah, while in later years, the connection was to be made even closer by the marriage of Joachim to a sister of Cornelius Vermuyden, Cornelia who died in the year 1612.

Reverting now to the proposals of 1593 of Humphrey Bradley for the drainage of the Great Level of the Fens, Bradley was a descendant in the direct line of those Zeelanders to whom reference has been made above and who had been called upon by the authorities of other countries to apply their knowledge of land reclamation problems to those countries. He had successfully worked in various parts of Europe, but his proposals for the Great Level failed to attract the approval of the Privy Council in spite of undoubtedly favourable terms upon which he was prepared to undertake the work. If the truth must be told, it is likely that Bradley's failure was primarily due to a reluctance on the part of the English to permit a foreigner to trespass on what they consider their preserves, and thus to reap the financial benefit, illusory though this was to prove in the end. The introduction of the Act of 1585, and the consequent evidence of the interest of the Crown in the matter of Fen reclamation, was doubtless the cause of Bradley's proposal, but, apart from the antipathy to foreign interference, there was, and would be for many years, strong opposition to any form of land reclamation on the part of the small landowners themselves, and of the commoners on those lands, realising as they did that the benefits to be gained would largely accrue to the 'adventurers' who treated an undertaking as a financial speculation only. This position was best summed up by Lord Willoughby in a letter which he wrote to the Earl of Essex in 1597 concerning the General Drainage Act of 1585. Willoughby himself certainly stood to gain from the draining of his fenland estates, but was altruistic enough to express his general disapproval of the Bill in the following terms. 'The bill promiseth fayre as a sunn shine daye that towards night setts with a tempest. I may mistake it, bycause I neither have nor cann see it, being in Mr. Atturneis hand, but as I hear it, it pretendeth to inable and releve a multitude of pore men for her Majesties service and the Commonwelths good by dreaning of sunkenn grounds and making that pasture which is fenn.' He then went on to say that by the time the various 'adventurers' in the drainage undertaking had been recompensed for their work by grants of part of the reclaimed land, certain of the commoners would have to be dispossessed of their rights of common. He added also that in those fens which were always drowned, and where when drained the rents would naturally be increased, it was questionable whether 'a poor man may not make more commodity of a fen full of fish, fowl and reed, rented for little or nothing, than of ground made pasture and improved to high rent, as the charges of the draining will require, for cattle and kine to feed on'.[1] Such laudable sentiments as these were certainly rare, indeed, sentiment entered little into the schemes of the adventurers, and when in 1606 Lord Chief Justice Popham, then an old man of seventy-five, was successful in his petition to be declared the undertaker for the draining of part of the Great Level, an anonymous correspondent of King James told him that the 'covetous and bloodie Popham' would ruin many poor men and that he, Popham, was cursed by all the poor in that part of England.[2]

We are not here concerned directly with the many applications made to the Privy Council for the privilege of tapping the imagined Eldorado of the Fens, mostly ill-conceived and over-optimistic, and the story of these is a long and involved one concerning a variety of individuals, a story which has been well told by Darby.[3] What we are concerned with is the interest in such schemes which prevailed in the Netherlands. Humphrey Bradley failed to obtain a sympathetic hearing. In 1606 Cornelius Liens and Cornelius Verneuil, the 'French Contractors' as they were termed in England, placed proposals before James for the draining of the Great Level, but while this application met the same fate as that of Humphrey Bradley, perhaps because of the greater influence of Popham, the proposal is significant because it represents the first real impact of the Great Level on the town of St. Maartensdijk and thus on the life of Cornelius Vermuyden. Of Cornelius Verneuil we know nothing. He may have been a Frenchman. Of Cornelius Liens we know quite a lot, and we know, of course, that he was a Netherlander, a Zeelander from St. Maartensdijk. Quite clearly Liens would have made his proposal to James only after the whole matter had been thrashed out in Zeeland with his associates in what was to be an 'onderneming', a co-operative undertaking financed in a manner similar to that which had been common for many years in the Netherlands. What the technical proposals comprised, what were the means by which the drainage was to be accomplished, we do not know, nor are we at this stage interested in such matters. The main factor was the financial organisation, and that was something of which these Netherlanders had valuable experience.

In the year 1609 an event occurred in the history of the Netherlands which was to have an abiding influence on the history of the draining of the Great Level and of Cornelius Vermuyden. In that year was concluded the Twelve Years' Truce in the interminable war with Spain. Now at the time of the signing of the truce Jacob Cats, born at Brouwershaven in the Isle of Schouwen in 1577, was building up the reputation which he later achieved

[1] H.M.C. Cd. 3429, Ancaster, pp. 337–8.
[2] *Cal. State Papers Dom. James I*, Vol. XIX., 47.
[3] *The Draining of the Fens*, *op. cit.*

of being, perhaps the most famous, or at least the most widely read, of the poets of the Netherlands. Cats was, however, more than a poet. He was a lawyer practising in Middleburg, and, what is more, he was a practical man of affairs. In 1611, two years after the signing of the truce, he, in partnership with his brother Cornelius, bought up at low prices land which had been flooded during the fighting as a strategical measure in the Staats-Vlanderen, and by draining and reclaiming this land was able eventually to dispose of it at considerable profit. On this basis was founded the large fortune which Jacob Cats was able to accumulate, and it was these circumstances which, somewhat naturally, fostered in his mind an interest in the profitable business of land reclamation. In 1605 Cats had married Elisabeth van Valckenburgh, a marriage not without its influence on the later career of Cornelius Vermuyden. But at the time of which we are now writing, the year 1611, Cornelius Vermuyden was a young man of twenty-one years living, presumably, in St. Maartensdijk, and occupied, perhaps, with the affairs of land reclamation in his native province of Zeeland. That must be mere presumption because there is no record of his activities in his early years. Indeed, in the Netherlands today Cornelius Vermuyden is known for what he did in England, and for that alone.

In England in 1618 occurred an event, or series of events, which might well be termed momentous in the history of draining of the Great Level. In that year the Commissioners of Sewers for the counties of Cambridge, Northampton, Huntingdon, Lincoln, Norfolk, and the Isle of Ely, came to the unanimous decision that one of the essentials for the drainage of the Great Level was the improvement of the outfalls of the River Ouse, Nene and Welland. The importance of this decision lies not in the matter of the remedy to be adopted, but in the fact that there was any decision unanimous to all the separate Commissioners of Sewers when hitherto there had always existed such a parochial outlook on the drainage of the Fens. On the petition presented to the Privy Council that 'a Clerk of the Council may be sent to their session as umpire, and all parties will abide by a constant and resolute course, to be taken upon his opinion'[1] Sir Clement Edmonds was appointed to meet the Commissioners and to report to the Council. Sir Clement, was, perhaps, well suited to conduct this enquiry because, while he was not what we should today term an engineer with specialised knowledge, he was a man of undoubted ability and had the advantage of having visited the Netherlands in 1614 as commissioner to discuss matters of the East India trade then in dispute between the United Provinces and His Majesty's government. Thus he may have had some knowledge of the

[1] *Cal. State Papers Dom. James I*, XCVII, 111.

reclamation schemes in the Netherlands. The instructions to Edmonds to meet the Commissioners of Sewers were given to him in June. On 12th August the meeting took place at Huntingdon, followed by a somewhat hurried visit to the outfalls, and on 20th September his report was presented to the Privy Council.[1] A commendably prompt piece of work. The substance of that report is here relatively unimportant, as are the subsequent investigations carried out on the instructions of the Privy Council by the Earl of Arundel, Sir William Ayloffe and Anthony Thomas, but the main point to bear in mind is that by this time the interest of many speculators in England had been aroused in the possibilities of the Fens. Indeed this interest was far from being confined to England. Jacob Cats, the Liens family, the van Valckenburgs, the van Peenens, and many other astute Netherlanders, with their wide experience of the practice of land reclamation, saw, perhaps much more clearly than the inexperienced Englishmen, the true nature of the problem in the Fens, and the financial needs to solve that problem. And when in 1618, the year of Sir Clement Edmonds' report, Joachim Liens, so closely connected to the Vermuyden family, came to England, the first step in Cornelius Vermuyden's career in the Great Level had been taken, although twelve years were still to pass before that step became decisive.

[1] *Acts of the Privy Council,* Jan. 1618 to June, 1619, pp. 292–299.

CHAPTER THREE

Interest of James I and influence on him of Joachim Liens. Arrival of Vermuyden in England. Roosevelt family in Isle of Tholen. Vermuyden's early work at Dagenham; his marriage.

BY the year 1618, when the Twelve Years Truce had still three more years to run, the Netherlands as represented mainly by the provinces of Holland and Zeeland had developed into one of the principal commercial powers of Europe with the city of Amsterdam predominant as a financial clearing house. It may be a fable of history to attribute the prosperity of the Netherlands in the seventeenth century to the exploitation of the East Indies, but there is no gainsaying that both the East India Company and the herring fisheries in the North Sea made considerable contributions to that prosperity. By the same token, both these industries were liable to create friction between the Netherlands and England whose interest in the two fields were inevitably bound to clash, particularly when King James of England was prone to issue decrees claiming the North Sea fishing grounds as part of his kingdom. Joachim Liens, the brother-in-law of Cornelius Vermuyden, came to England in 1618, in company with Edward van Dussen of Zutphen, and Jan van Goch of Delft, as a commissioner of the Netherlands Government to discuss with the English Government the affairs of the Dutch East India Company and also the matter of the herring fisheries, and on 13 July, 1619, Liens, 'a syndic of Tholen', and his two companions, were knighted by James at Theobalds.[1]

It is interesting to note that James throughout his reign of twenty-four years appears always to have had some partiality towards the adventure of land reclamation. As we have seen, the national interest in such matters had been aroused primarily by the Parliamentary Bill introduced in 1585. The subsequent activities of Sir William Russell, of Humphrey Bradley, of Cornelius Liens and Cornelius Verneuil, of Lord Chief Justice Popham, had all helped to keep the light focussed on the subject. When Liens came to England the activities of the Commissioners of Sewers in the East Anglian

[1] WM. A. SHAW, *The Knights of England*, 1906.

counties had once again brought the Great Level to the fore and James himself was showing interest in another part of the country, Sedgmoor in Somerset, where he had 'on the petition of the lords and tenants claiming right thereon, and on their acknowledgement of his right, consented to an improvement'[1] Thirty-five years later Sedgmoor itself was to play a part in the story of Cornelius Vermuyden, but in 1618–19 it was merely a pointer to the king's interest in the matter of land reclamation. But one is impelled to ask to what extent did Joachim Liens foster this interest for the purpose of furthering an imminent application for reclaiming the Great Level of the Fens which he knew his brother Cornelius Liens and other Zeelanders had in mind. Cornelius had, of course, tried unsuccessfully in 1606 and since then there is little doubt that the matter had remained conspicuously in the minds of the astute Zeelanders.

Joachim Liens was fully aware that there were many others in England, and also outside it, who had similar ideas to those of his brother. Sir William Ayloffe and Anthony Thomas, having carried out their inspection of the Great Level on behalf of the Privy Council, themselves petitioned the Council for the right to drain the Level, their petition being presented in July 1619 the very month in which Joachim Liens was being knighted. Ayloffe and Thomas were very strong contenders for the privilege of risking their money, and that of their associates, in the unpredictable swamps of the Great Level and two months after their first petition had been presented, and while the stumbling block to any settlement appeared to be the question, vital to James, of the Crown rents payable on the reclaimed lands, they informed the King that they were quite prepared to leave this question to be settled later. James no doubt saw in this his opportunity for a subsequent favourable outcome to his financial bargaining and thus instructed the Privy Council to come to terms with Ayloffe and Thomas. Another year passed and in November 1620 these persistent 'adventurers' had achieved nothing definite from the Council and complained bitterly that although they had ridden 10,000 miles and expended £2,400 no final decision had by then been reached in their favour.[2]

It is not unreasonable to perceive in this delay the influence of James himself because, as events were to prove, he was anxious to become the 'undertaker' in person, but there is also the question, which the Privy Council itself posed, as to what methods, what scheme of drainage, Ayloffe and Thomas intended to put into execution for the drainage of the Level. There is no evidence to show that they had any concrete plan and there are

[1] *Cal. State Papers Dom.* 1655. Vol. C. p. 301.
[2] *Cal. State Papers Dom. James I*, Vol. CXVIII, 78.

indeed grounds for the suspicion that their chief concern was the monetary gain without much heed for the complicated and widespread practical activities lacking which that gain was an impossibility. At that time there was little, if any, understanding on the part of prospective adventurers of how imperative was the need for a planned and organised system if the immense tract of over three hundred thousand acres of marshy Fenland was to be reclaimed from the waters. Any haphazard digging of ditches would accomplish nothing. But, of course, the experienced men of the Netherlands were fully alive to all the difficulties which faced any undertaking, and while Joachim Liens was in England primarily as an official envoy, unofficially he was taking an intense interest in the moves taking place in and around the Great Level, and, no doubt, was keeping his brother Cornelius fully informed. How far he was hoping for favour and help from James it is impossible to say, but in February, 1621, James disappointed all hopes by declaring himself the undertaker saying that 'he would not any longer suffer these countries to be abandoned to the will of the waters',[1] and reserving to himself the recompense of 120,000 acres of the reclaimed land.

It was, however, one thing to pronounce oneself the undertaker in a project of this nature but another to find the financial means and devise the practical methods by which the project could be put into effect. As far as the financial side was concerned James had no resources upon which he could draw. At least, he had no official resources because the Treasury was at that time in no more prosperous condition than it normally was in Stuart times. How far, then, was James prompted to make this declaration by promises of financial support made to him by Joachim Liens on behalf of the latter's associates in the Netherlands? Dugdale is completely silent on this point. But we cannot ignore entirely the implications contained in an event of outstanding importance to the Great Level which occurred in 1621. In that year Cornelius Vermuyden arrived in England. Now Vermuyden was in later years to write that 'When K. James, of blessed memory, undertook the drayning of the Great Level as aforesaid, at that time I was come over to England, invited to this work',[2] but that statement does not prove conclusively by whom he was so invited, by James himself or by Joachim Liens. The natural conclusion is, however, that the invitation came directly, or indirectly, from the latter, and, consequently, that Liens had come to an agreement with James for the financing of the undertaking by capital from the Netherlands. In the end, of course, the intentions of James remained

[1] W. Dugdale, *The History of Imbanking and Draining*, 2nd ed., 1772, p. 407.

[2] *Discourse Touching the Drayning of the Great Fennes*, 1642.

nothing more than intentions, and, as Dugdale puts it, 'whether it was the great disturbance he had about that time, and after until the end of his reign, for regaining the Palatinate, then violently invaded by a powerful army, and his daughter, with her husband and children, exposed to the wide world for a subsistence, which was the impediment; or what else, I shall not take upon me to say.'[1] The inactivity on the part of the king was most galling to the Netherlanders and in 1622, in the hope of forcing some definite action, Cornelius Liens again put forward a proposal for an undertaking, it will be remembered that he had made his original proposal in 1606 in company with Cornelius Verneuil, this time naming Cornelius Vermuyden as his co-undertaker. All this was of no avail and the Great Level was to lie undisturbed for another eight years before the first, and last, reclamation scheme, that of Cornelius Vermuyden, was to be commenced.

The year 1621 was one of some considerable import to the Netherlands because in that year ended the Twelve Years' Truce and once more the struggle against the Spanish domination commenced. The war was bound to restrict to some degree the work of land reclamation in the country and it may be that lack of employment in such work was the reason for Cornelius Vermuyden at that time being employed as a tax collector in the town of Tholen.[2] To him, therefore, the call to England from Joachim Liens must have been more than welcome, and with his arrival in this country began an active career extending over thirty-five years, a career to be characterised by restless energy, supreme achievement, fame, or as his many adversaries would call it, notoriety, all to end in almost complete obscurity. Up to the time of his coming to England we know nothing about Vermuyden other than the fact of his birth, and even the date of that is debatable, and the isolated incidents connecting him with the town of St. Maartensdijk and with the Liens family. We are ignorant entirely of his practical and professional experience of methods of land reclamation and drainage yet one is compelled to assume that his talents in these lines were worthy of respect as otherwise Cornelius and Joachim Liens, and the other later 'adventurers' in the Netherlands, would not have been willing to entrust their heavy investments in Hatfield Chase and in the Great Level in his hands.

To say that today the existence of modern Holland implies a constant struggle against the sea and the inland waters is to state a commonplace, but the need for constant vigilance and supervision of embankments was even greater in the sixteenth and seventeenth centuries than in our present times.

[1] W. Dugdale, *op. cit.*, p. 407.
[2] F. Nagtglas, *Levensberichten van Zeeuwen.* Middelburg, 1890–3.

The whole of the province of Zeeland, generally as it exists today with its group of scattered islands, had been created by the breaking in of the North Sea through the protective line of sand dunes forming in earlier times a barrier along the coast similar to that which now runs northward in an unbroken line from the Hook of Holland right up to Den Helder below the Isle of Texel.

Disastrous inundations when thousands of acres of land were lost, when villages and towns with their inhabitants were destroyed, happened long before Vermuyden's time, but the Zeelanders of his time were traditionally aware of these catastrophies and he himself must have been fully acquainted with the inundation in, or about, the year 1570 of the large tract of land, the Reimerswaal, which lay just south-east of the town of St. Maartensdijk between the Isle of Tholen and South Beveland, and which still lies covered by the waters of the Ooster Schelde.

Some time about the middle of the sixteenth century Andries Vierlingh, who has been described as the greatest of Dutch 'dike-masters', wrote his treatise 'Tractaet van Dijckagie'[1] in which for the first time were laid down principles of land drainage and for the building of dykes, principles which must have had their influence on Vermuyden and his contemporaries. When the first breach in the dyke at Reimerswaal occurred Vierlingh visited the spot and warned Adriaan van Reimerswaal, Lord of the Manor of Lodijke, that if prompt measures were taken the breach could be repaired, but if not the whole of the land would be lost. His advice went unheeded and as he had predicted the whole of the area was eventually inundated.

The story of the loss of the Reimerswaal has little, if anything, to do with the story of Cornelius Vermuyden, except in so far as the memory of the disaster was fresh in the minds, and even in the sight, of his elders and must have exercised some influence on his own philosophy of the hazards of land reclamation. Curiously enough, and if we may digress for a while, it had some considerable bearing on the modern history of the United States of America.

In the Waterschap of Oud-Vossemeer in the Isle of Tholen, between the towns of Tholen and Portvliet and only a few miles distant from the town of St. Maartensdijk, there lay in the seventeenth century an area known as the Roosevelt, or Rose Field. Today in the church of Tholen can be seen a gravestone commemorating the burial of one Marinus van Roosevelt, 'in his life Burgomaster of this town, "leenman" of the province of Zeeland, Dijkgraf of Glimes, who died on the 29th January 1710, and of his wife Joanna Poulier who died 11th May 1707'. The origin of this family 'van

[1] *Rijks Geschiedskundige Publicatien,* Kleine Serie 20. 'S-Gravenhage, 1920.

Roosevelt' or 'of the Rose Field', is somewhat obscure, but it is an established fact that in the year 1573 one Cornelis Jorisz (from the Roosevelt) acted as guardian to the children of Dyne Claesz. Piersz., and in the records of that period one reads frequently of the 'hoefje', the small-holding and farmhouse, 'op 't Roosevelt' between Tholen and Portvliet. This 'hoefje' had belonged to Cornelis Jorisz. 'op 't Roosevelt' who was married to Marikens Jacobs. After his death the widow married Leunis Stoffels and in 1589 Stoffels decided to sell the 'hoefje' to Corten Huybrechts for demolition because, as he said, 'the soldiers had damaged it.'[1]

It is now generally accepted that the family 'op 't Roosevelt', who in time adopted the surname of Roosevelt, came originally to the Isle of Tholen from the Reimerswaal as refugees from the disastrous floods there of 1570. This may be partly speculation, but what is quite certain is that in the year 1649 one Claes Roosevelt, 'of the Isle of Tholen', sailed from Delfshaven for North America where he settled in the Dutch town of New Amsterdam, later to become New York. From Claes Roosevelt sprang the famous American family and two Presidents of the United States.

The story of the family 'op 't Roosevelt' has less to do with the story of Cornelius Vermuyden than has the Reimerswaal, but it is highly probable that the Roosevelts were well acquainted with the Vermuydens, even though Claes Roosevelt himself left the Netherlands twenty-eight years after Cornelius Vermuyden's departure, and when the latter, as we shall show later, was nearing the end of his career in the Great Level. That is, of course, assuming that Vermuyden first arrived in England in 1621, an assumption based on fairly sound evidence, but there is in existence a very improbable story that he arrived in England long before the year 1621. There is very little, if any, evidence to support this story but it is, perhaps, of interest to examine it briefly as an example of the kind of imaginative stories which have been built round the name of Vermuyden, and eventually accepted as true merely by virtue of constant repetition.

The first work of major importance which Vermuyden carried out in England was the drainage of Hatfield Chase in Yorkshire which he began in 1626. We shall deal with this work in some detail later on, but now we must take it somewhat out of its turn to relate how, at the end of the seventeenth century, Abraham de la Pryme, rector of Thorne on the borders of the Chase, left behind when he died a manuscript 'History of Hatfield Chase'.[2] De la Pryme was the son of one of the original adventurers in the drainage undertaking who had come from the Netherlands and who, there-

[1] C. VELTENAAR. *De Geschiedenis van Tholen*, Middelburg, 1943.

[2] *Landsdowne MSS.* 897. British Museum.

fore, was well acquainted with Cornelius Vermuyden, and he relates in his *History* how Prince Henry, the eldest son of James I, had in 1609 attended a hunting party in Hatfield Chase on his way to York. He describes how Henry stayed one night at Streethorpe in the Level of Hatfield at the house of Sir Robert Swift, a local landowner, and goes on to give details of the hunting party which took place the following day. This may all be true, and there seems no reason why de la Pryme should invent the story, but a later writer has expressed some doubt as to whether Prince Henry was at Hatfield in 1609 and states that 'in the course of laborious enquiries . . . into the royal progresses of the reign of King James, nothing has presented itself which afforded current proof with this testimony of de la Pryme to a visit of Prince Henry at Hatfield in 1609. He was certainly with the King at Farnham, the Bishop of Winchester's on the 24th July, and he is to be traced in and near London during the greater part of the year.'[1]

One hundred and thirty-three years after de la Pryme had recorded his story, Samuel Wells, without quoting any authority to support his statement, wrote that 'Vermuyden was in the suite of this Prince on the occasion of the hunt',[2] while nine years later Stonehouse further elaborated the fable by declaring that 'During this celebrated hunting there rode in the train of that Royal Prince a phlegmatic Dutchman who beheld the scene before him not so much with the eye of a sportsman as with a view to turning the country to his own profit: this person was Cornelius Vermuyden, who is said to have then first conceived the idea of draining the whole Level. This happened in the year 1609'[3] Even if we accept the truth of de la Pryme's statement of the hunting expedition itself having occurred, and it will be seen that there is a certain amount of doubt as to whether Prince Henry could have been there, there does not exist the slightest shred of evidence to support the fanciful story of Samuel Wells concerning Vermuyden's presence, which story in the end gave rise to Stonehouse's almost factual relation of the machinations of the 'phlegmatic Dutchman'. The sober conclusion is that having related the story of the hunting expedition, if Vermuyden had been there, de la Pryme would have said so, since Vermuyden and his father had been so intimately connected, and thus it is wiser to accept the fact that Cornelius Vermuyden first came to England in 1621 at the invitation, direct or indirect, of Joachim Liens.

The persuasive arguments which, apparently, Joachim Liens was placing before James for the draining of the Great Level had no effect on the king

[1] JOSEPH HUNTER, *South Yorkshire*, 1828, Vol. I, p. 156. Note 4.
[2] SAMUEL WELLS, *The History of the Bedford Level*, Vol. 1, p. 93, 1830.
[3] W. B. STONEHOUSE, *The History and Topography of the Isle of Axholme*, p. 73, 1839.

distracted by the many problems facing him at that time, and, in the meantime it was necessary for Cornelius Vermuyden, now that he had come to England, to find something to do. It is quite clear that the restless energy of the man, to be demonstrated so clearly in his later years, would not permit him to wait idly in England while the seemingly interminable discussions on the Great Level went on and on. Some time soon after his arrival in 1621 Vermuyden was engaged by the Commissioners of Sewers for the County of Essex for the repairs to the breach in the banks of the Thames at Dagenham and in all probability the Commissioners made the appointment on the prompting of James himself. Admittedly that is largely a matter of surmise but, as later events were to show, Court influence was something which was often exercised in the interests of Vermuyden, particularly in the subsequent reign of Charles I.

The breach in the banks of the Thames at Dagenham, and the consequent flooding of the Levels of Dagenham and Havering had occurred in, or before, the year 1593 when it was alleged at a Session of Sewers held at Romford that the 'drowning' had been occasioned by a breach in the wall belonging to one William Ayloffe of Hornchurch (not Sir William Ayloffe mentioned earlier in connection with the Great Level). Repairs were carried out on the instructions of the Commissioners, but in September 1621 a breach again occurred, 'These banks being not made strong enough to withstand those tempestuous storms and violent tides, which happened in the month of September.'[1] The date usually given for Vermuyden's contract for this repair work is the year 1621, but in 1623 the Commissioners of Sewers were reporting that it was 'before Michaelmas last', i.e. in 1622 that the contract was made, and, therefore, probably after the abortive joint application which Cornelius Liens and Vermuyden had made in 1622 for the work in the Great Level. However, that is of comparatively little importance. What is of importance is that in their report of 1623 the Commissioners were emphatic in saying that by February, the month in which they were writing, and when, presumably, the work should have been completed, Vermuyden 'not only has accomplished little hitherto, but by his delays and the want of durability in the works he has accomplished, the land is in worse condition than it was before.[2]

Now subsequent events one hundred years later were to prove that the closing of a breach in the river bank at Dagenham was a very costly and hazardous undertaking and when in 1722 Captain John Perry completed his contract for carrying out the work the amount which he had expended

[1] W. Dugdale, *op. cit.*, p. 81.
[2] *Cal. State Papers Dom. James I*, Vol. CXXXVIII, p. 486

was no less than £40,000.[1] Even allowing for the difference in the value of money in the years 1622 and 1722 this was a vastly different sum from the £2,000 which was the amount of Vermuyden's contract. Possibly the extent of the breach in 1622 was considerably less than that with which Perry had to contend, but there remains the suspicion that Vermuyden had been guilty of under-estimating the amount of work involved, and thus of carrying out works lacking in 'durability', as the Commissioners alleged. Before the Commissioners report Vermuyden had been called before the Privy Council to answer complaints received by the Council from his workmen that they were unable to obtain payment of their wages. Vermuyden's reply was that although the value of his contract was £2,000, and while he had, in fact, expended £3,600, he had received nothing from the Commissioners and was quite prepared to pay the workmen when the Commissioners paid him.[2] The true facts of the case are rather difficult to unravel and the situation is somewhat complicated by a petition presented to the Privy Council some time in 1622 by one Arian Yonge Johnston, and sixty-two other workmen, who had been employed by another contractor, John Foster, on similar work at Dagenham. The petition stated that the workmen were unable to obtain their wages because John Foster had to abandon his contract when part of his work 'gave way' owing to 'the decay of Mr. Vermuyden's portion'.[3]

There may have been nothing in the complaints and allegations of the Commissioners of Sewers. These may have been due to antagonism to a foreigner or resentment that a nominee of the Court had been forced on them for the work. On the other hand, the Commissioners were men of substance and integrity, and, even if only from the independent testimony of Arian Yonge Johnston, there appears to be evidence that Vermuyden's work was defective. And thus it is possible, and permissible, to conclude that Vermuyden's first employment was not entirely a success, and that, indeed, it would not have been surprising if that first employment had been the last. In fact, of course, this was far from being the case and while the Commissioners steadfastly refused to pay anything of the contract price to Vermuyden, James was in 1623 employing him on the work of draining Windsor Park, certainly a work of a very minor nature, and in July 1625 the Crown confirmed the grant to Vermuyden of certain lands at Dagenham as recompense for the work which he had carried out.[4] That was at the

[1] J. Perry, *An Account of the Stopping of Dagenham Breach*, 1721.
[2] *Acts of the Privy Council, July 1621*—May 1623, p. 377.
[3] *Cal. State Papers Dom.*, James I, Vol. CXLVII, p. 475.
[4] *Ibid*, Charles I. Vol. IV.

instance of Charles I who had succeeded James some four months previously. And the explanation of all this must surely be that Vermuyden was in the favour of the Court by virtue of the influence exerted by his brothers-in-law, Joachim and Cornelius Liens. Certainly by the end of the year 1623 he had accomplished nothing in England—and we have no knowledge of what he had done in the Netherlands—to justify any special confidence in his practical ability. If, however, the Royal favour did aid him at the start of his career, it should be clear from the relation of his later years that the successes which he achieved, however much they may have been decried by his enemies, were the result of his own dynamic and restless ability allied to something near to genius. All this was many years ahead but in November 1623, Vermuyden considered himself sufficiently established to take a wife and on the 6th of that month was married to Katherine, daughter of All-saints Lapps (or Laps) Merchant, of London, at Rotherhithe on the Surrey bank of the Thames. On the same day Anne, sister of Katherine married at the same church Jacob Struwys (or Struys) another Netherlander.

It has hitherto in the past been assumed that the Laps family were of English descent, but more recent evidence tends to disprove this assumption. It is shown in the archives of the Dutch Reformed Church of Austin Friars that on 1st January, 1594, a certain Toussain Lap of Bruges (later described as Laps) married Catherine Houwe of Cassel and that this Catherine on 13th September, 1614, married as her third husband Joos Croppenburgh. From this it appears to be clear that the Laps family were natives of the Netherlands, while the mention of Joos Croppenburgh brings in a further connection with the Vermuyden family. On 16th June, 1622, Joos Croppenburgh signed an indenture under the terms of which he was 'at his own costs to Inne or cause to be Inned', all the lands, except 14 acres, in 'Erith co. Kent called the great breach containing 492 acres which have been for years subject to flooding by the Thames'.[1] This indenture is quoted in a Chancery Suit of 5th November, 1626, filed by one William Finch and Jonathan Brett against Vermuyden and Croppenburgh. The subject of the suit is not of importance, but its importance lies in the fact that the plea states that 'Cornelius Vermuyden of London, gent. assisted [Croppenburgh]'. Incidentally, Croppenburgh, on 9th April, 1622, had entered into a contract with Sir Henry Appleton for the embanking and reclaiming of flooded lands in Canvey Island in the lower reaches of the Thames. Vermuyden's association with Croppenburgh was understandable because, apart from the fact of their being both Netherlanders, Croppenburgh had married as his second wife, after the death of Catherine, Mary Vermuyden, a daughter of Johan

[1] *Chancery Proceedings*, C.2., Chas. I., F.44-45.

Vermuyden, son of Cornelius Vermuyden's elder brother Bartholomew. It has sometimes been suggested that Vermuyden's introduction to King James came through the agency of Joos Croppenburgh. Certainly their association was by the nature of things close, but it is considered that the conclusion that the source of this introduction was Joachim Liens is the more reasonable.

CHAPTER FOUR

Hatfield Chase. Death of James I. Vermuyden's agreement with Charles I for drainage of the Chase. Principles of his scheme; comparison with polder reclamation in Holland. Its financing.

THE Level of the Royal Chase of Hatfield lies a few miles east of Doncaster and on the Yorkshire-Lincolnshire borders, occupying some 70,000 acres of country of a nature very similar to that of the drowned lands of the Fens. According to de la Pryme it was King James himself who conceived the idea of draining the Chase, part of the Crown lands, 'both for the profit of himself and the country'. Even if Vermuyden had never been in Hatfield Chase in 1609 it would not be difficult to imagine that both he and his sponsors in the Netherlands were fully alive to the possibilities existing there, and were ready for any opportunity to exploit these. In 1621 James had been disappointed in his spacious gesture of declaring himself undertaker for the drainage of the Great Level, from which his attention had been distracted by events on the Continent and the troubles of his son-in-law, Frederic the Elector Palatinate. It is also reasonable to suppose that James may have been somewhat daunted by the magnitude of the Fen undertaking, although nobody at that time had a clear appreciation of the difficulties there, and thus may have come to the conclusion that the easier, and safer course would be to start with something smaller. Certainly Vermuyden was there to advise him, and persuade him, as to the advantages to be gained, and, what is more, he was there to press the claims of his associates in the Netherlands anxious and willing to provide the essential for which James himself could make no provision, finance.

In 1622 James appointed a Committee to enquire, as de la Pryme puts it, 'into the state of the said Chase, whether his tenants have not forfeited his favour of Commoning therein by building new houses upon it, joysting beasts upon it, cutting down the trees thereof, and destroying his game; likewise they were to consider about the Draining, Improving, and disafforestation thereof'. The Commission consisted of landowners in the neighbourhood of the Chase headed by Sir Robert Swift and Godfrey Copley, and in due course they reported to the King confirming his fears that he 'was encroached upon, his favours abused, his Chase joysted, in, etc.', but much to James's disappointment they went on to express the opinion that 'considering how great the Levels were, and how continually deep with water, how many rivers run thereunto, and such like, they did humbly conceive that it was impossible to drain and improve them'. Sir Robert Swift, it will be recalled, was said to have been host to Prince Henry in 1609 when he had taken part in the disputed hunting expedition in Hatfield Chase, and doubtless Sir Robert and his fellow Commissioners occasionally indulged in a little quiet 'joysting' on their own account when the eye of Royalty was not upon them. Consequently they may have looked with some disfavour on the proposition to drain and dis-afforest the Chase as this course would deprive them of periodic unlawful sport and supplies of venison. Their verdict on the impracticability of the draining may, therefore, have been tinged somewhat with self interest.

James, however, was not prepared to accept this verdict without further consideration, and in asking Cornelius Vermuyden to examine the report on the matter was automatically committing himself to a report that the drainage proposition was perfectly feasible, and while there is, unfortunately, no remaining written report from Vermuyden, there is evidence that he did report in this sense. But once again external circumstances were too much for James. There were the negotiations for the Spanish marriage, there was the Spanish War of 1624, and then the negotiations for the marriage of Charles to Henrietta Maria, all of which called for attention to the exclusion of drainage matters. And before anything could be done about Hatfield Chase, on 27th March, 1625 James died.

Hatfield Chase, of comparatively small extent, may at first sight appear to be somewhat irrelevant to the story of Cornelius Vermuyden and the Great Level of the Fens, but, in fact, the drainage of this area, which was eventually undertaken, proved to be an important influence in the life of Vermuyden. The reputation which he made there, and, one might say, the notoriety which he gained there, were important factors in influencing his later employment in the Great Level. Furthermore, the principles on which Vermuyden based his scheme in Hatfield Chase, whether they were right or wrong, became the principles adopted by him in the Great Level and, therefore, were to determine the course of land drainage and reclamation in England for several hundreds of years. On this account, therefore, it is necessary to have some understanding, not only of the outline of his technical principles in Hatfield Chase, but also of the difficulties and opposition which he met there, and which, possibly, influenced the development of his own character. Certainly the manner in which he faced the opposition gives us some basis on which to assess that character of which we have so little direct evidence.

The death of James could not have come as a surprise to Vermuyden, or, indeed, to anybody else, in view of the chronic state of ill-health in which the King had existed for so many years. On the other hand, it may have appeared at first sight to be something of a set-back after all the persuasive arguments which Vermuyden had advanced, and which had all but reached a successful climax. But a man as astute as Vermuyden could not have been unprepared for this likely eventuality. Doubtless King Charles was fully aware of the Hatfield Chase negotiations before his father's death and when he succeeded to the throne it is quite possible that the anticipated financial benefits to the Royal Treasury may have had an even greater appeal to the new monarch than they had had to James. Cornelius Vermuyden had a powerful ally at Court in the person of Sir Robert Heath, Attorney-General in Charles's reign from 1625 until appointed Chief Justice of Common Pleas in 1631. Heath and Vermuyden were in later years to be associated in many an enterprise—their joint undertaking in the lead mines at Wirksworth in Derbyshire is one example—and there is in the State Papers a significant document in the handwriting of Heath, undated but presumably written in 1625, entitled 'Remembrance for the King's services at my going to Court' in which he sets out methods of increasing the revenues by some £150,000 per annum 'by letting the land of recusants, laying a tax on foreign fisheries, making new arrangements respecting madder, Virginian tobacco, the manufacture of soap, draining the fens, and disafforesting distant forests'.[1] In the reference to 'draining the fens' it is possible to see the hand of Vermuyden, but whether the finally persuasive arguments came from him or from Heath is immaterial. What is material is that on 24th May, 1626, just over one year after James's death, Charles signed an agreement with Cornelius Vermuyden for the drainage of Hatfield Chase.[2]

The Hatfield Chase 'undertaking' could more truly be referred to as an 'onderneming' because, with two exceptions, it was financed entirely from the Netherlands on the pattern which had for so long been in use in that country. The agreement was between 'our Sovereign Lord the King's Majesty, of the one part, and Cornelius Vermuyden, of London, esquire, of the other part', but while Vermuyden was the principal undertaker, he was, of course, acting only as agent for the other participants, each of whom

[1] *Cal. State Papers Dom.* Charles I., Vol. XLIV.I.

[2] The original of this agreement is in the possession of the Trent River Board, Nottingham.

was to benefit from the profits of the undertaking in proportion to his contribution to the capital fund. That profit was to comprise 'one full third part in three parts, to be divided of all and singular the said surrounded and waste grounds' and the total acreage so to be allotted amounted to 24,405 acres, of which Vermuyden's share was 4,554 acres. This must be considered at least partly as payment for his services as director of the works because it is not to be expected that Vermuyden would have been in a position to invest a sum proportionate to this allotment. Curiously enough an examination of the list of the original participants fails to reveal any mention of the Liens family. They may, of course, have had an interest in Vermuyden's allotment. Jacob Cats was a very minor participant with an allotment of only 67 acres, but his nephew, Leonard, participated to the extent of 200 acres while the three brothers Matthew, Marcus and Lucas van Valckenburg, of the family of Jacob Cat's wife, had a total holding of 3,204 acres. Other significant names among the participants, of whom there were 35 in all, were those of Philibert Vernatti, to be closely associated later with the Great Level, and of Jacob Struys who had figured with Vermuyden in the double wedding of the two Laps sisters at Rotherhithe in 1623.

An examination of some of the principal clauses of the agreement between Charles and Vermuyden reveals that it imposed no arduous conditions likely to endanger the financial success of the undertaking. Firstly, the agreement specified that 'the said Cornelius Vermuyden doth hereby promise and undertake that he will do his best endeavour . . . to drain and lay dry the said drowned and surrounded grounds in such manner as to make the same fit for tillage or pasture'. Secondly, 'the said Cornelius Vermuyden doth hereby further promise, covenant and grant to and with our said sovereign lord the King, that he . . . shall and will set on workmen and begin the said work within three months next after our sovereign lord the King's Majesty shall have agreed and concluded with such person or persons as shall have claim to drain any estate, interest, or common of or in the said grounds'. Thirdly, it was stipulated that Vermuyden should finish the work of draining 'with as much convenient expedition as possible may be'. He was granted practically a free hand in the use of existing watercourses, in the construction of new channels, and was empowered to acquire any lands which were considered necessary for this purpose at rates of compensation to the owners to be determined by a commission of four members, two to be appointed by the Lord High Treasurer, and two by Vermuyden himself. Permission was granted for the import of any materials 'necessary to be brought out of the low countries, or from any parts beyond the seas' without the payment of duty.

Taking all factors into consideration it is clear that the agreement was a most equitable one and, indeed, most favourable to the participants. There was no specified time for the completion of the contract, there were no penalties involved, and the one stipulation regarding the date for the commencement of the work placed the onus for determining this on the King himself by his conclusion of an agreement with the commoners and other interested parties. The question of the rights of commoners on 'drowned' or 'surrounded' grounds is one on which we have earlier briefly touched. It was a question which was to pervade the whole of the early history of Fen drainage and which, in the case of Hatfield Chase, was to assume such proportions as to influence the whole success or failure of the scheme from the financial point of view. But before dealing with this factor let us consider some aspects of the undertaking from the technical point of view.

One of the clauses of the agreement stated that it was agreed 'that the said Cornelius Vermuyden, and other the parties by him to be employed as aforesaid, in all such places as he or they shall think fit, necessary, and expedient, shall and may leave without the said work and grounds so to be by him and them gained as aforesaid, some small parcels of land on each or either sides of the said several rivers, for receptacles of the sudden downfalls of waters'. Thus was embodied, doubtless at the desire of Vermuyden, the principle of 'washes', which if it did not initially affect the work at Hatfield, was a principle to which he was to adhere in his scheme for the Great Level of the Fens where it became, and has always remained, a matter of extreme controversy. Some understanding of the use, and principle, of washes is, therefore desirable.

Where the land through which a river is flowing is flat, and where, therefore, the river has a flat gradient, in times of heavy rain or of rapidly melting snow there will be a tendency for the waters to overflow their banks and flood an area on one or both sides of the stream simply for the reason that, owing to the flat gradient, and hence the comparatively sluggish flow, the waters cannot reach the outfall quickly enough to prevent over-topping of the banks. These flooded areas are known as the natural flood plain of the river. Vermuyden's principle of 'washes' was, as he was later to say, 'to imitate nature' and to supplement the flood plains of the rivers flowing through the Hatfield Level by the provision of 'receptacles for the water in time of extremity to bed on upon all occasions of floods, and so to keep the waters at a lesser height by far against the banks'.[1] This principle of washes was not really to be challenged until Vermuyden was engaged in the much larger scheme in the Great Level when, in addition, he had to face the

[1] *Discourse.*

charge of adopting methods of draining which, however suitable they might be for the conditions prevailing in the Netherlands, should not have been applied to the different conditions in England, and in the Fens in particular. Now when Vermuyden devised and carried out his scheme of drainage in Hatfield Chase he had not, as far as we know, had experience in the designing of a scheme of similar extent in Zeeland, and certainly not in England. Thus, to some extent, he may have been experimenting with his methods, but for him to fail to see the fundamental difference between the general conditions of polder reclamation in the Netherlands—and his experience was likely to have been mainly on such polder reclamation—would have been foolish in the extreme, and Vermuyden was no fool. As, therefore, the principles and methods which he adopted in Hatfield Chase were essentially those to be adopted later in the Great Level, it will be as well to examine briefly that fundamental difference upon which his appreciation of the situation was based.

In Plate 2 are shown two maps of the 'waterschap', or drainage district, of St. Maartensdijk, that on the left indicating its state in the thirteenth century, that on the right showing it in its present state.[1] In the thirteenth-century the 'waterschap' of St. Maartensdijk consisted of one polder only, the Oudeland, but, as time went on, gradually the inhabitants of this and other precarious footholds in the Isle of Tholen extended their possessions in the delta formation by the creation, the wresting from the sea, of new polders. The process was a simple one. The area of silt chosen for reclamation, washed each day by the tides, was at the lowest ebb embanked and as each successive tide brought in new silt deposits so the surface rose until, finally, the embankments were raised above the highest flood tide, the water inside these was pumped out by primitive baling appliances until at last the new polder stood dry and reclaimed from the sea. Now it is not suggested that polder reclamation was the sole drainage activity in the Netherlands. It was, indeed, more an embankment activity than draining, but it is probable that polder reclamation was the problem with which Vermuyden was most familiar, and he must be given the credit for seeing that what he was faced with in Hatfield Chase was essentially different and, therefore, called for different methods. The problem there was that created by the rivers Don, Torne, Idle, Aire, Went and Bewcarrsdyke, as they wandered slowly and tortuously through the Level, periodically flooding the surrounding land and creating wastes and marshes, half water, half land. And this was basically a drainage problem.

Vermuyden's reasoning on the problem at Hatfield appears to have been quite sound, judged only on the work which he did as, unfortunately, there

[1] A. Hollestelle, *op. cit.*

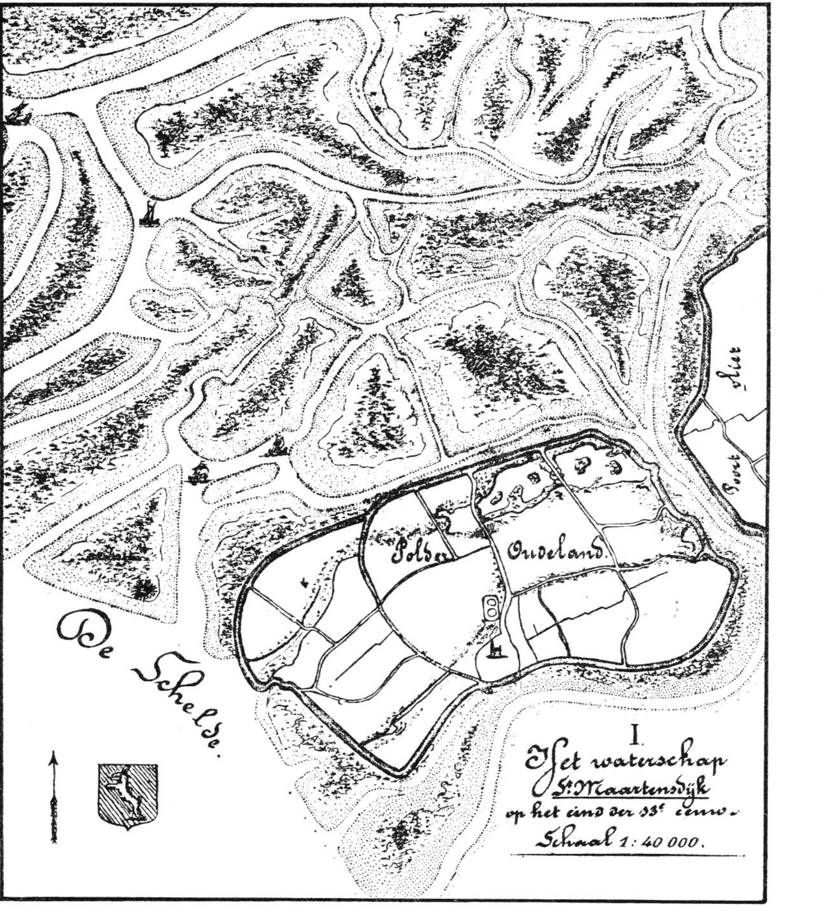

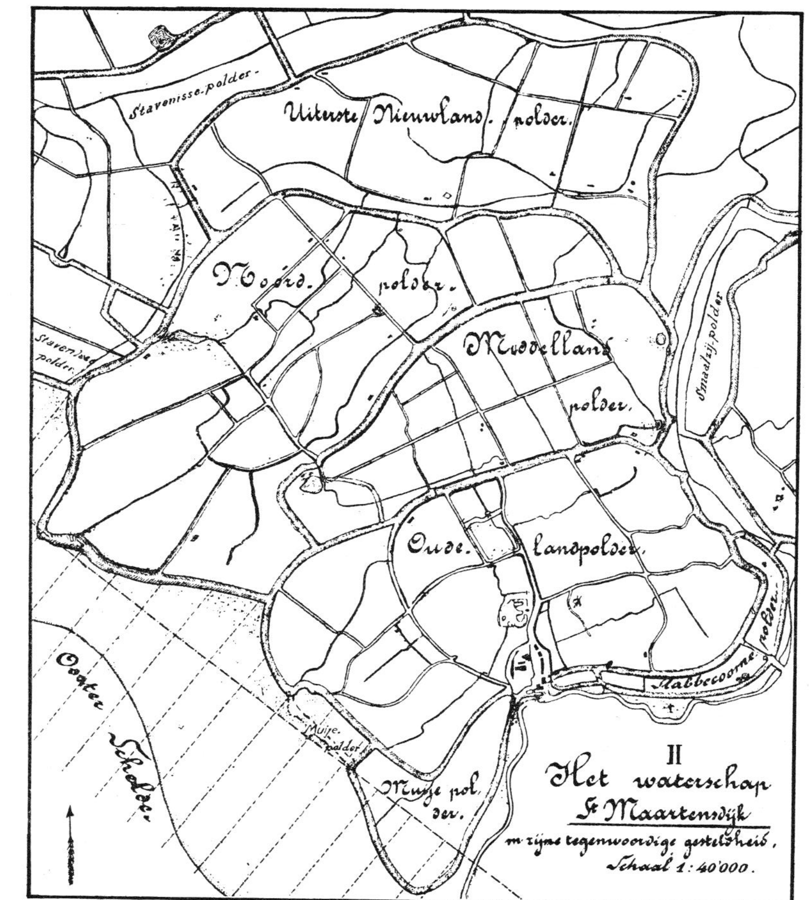

Plate II. The 'Waterschap' of St. Maartensdijk (*left*) at the end of the 13th century, (*right*) at the present time

From A. Hollestelle : *Het Eiland Tholen* (Tholen, Zeeland, 1919).

is no written record of his intentions there such as has survived for his later, and greater, work in the Great Level of the Fens. Briefly it can be said that his theory was, firstly, that the river Don with its three branches was the main contributory cause of the flooding, and, secondly, that in the case of all the rivers the remedy was to cut new straight channels where necessary to replace the natural winding courses, a remedy to which he was later also to adhere in the Great Level. It is not proposed here to explain in any detail the work which he actually carried out in Hatfield Chase as we are more concerned with the principles upon which he based his practice, and their influence on his later work in the Great Level. Even if, as has been assumed, Vermuyden's personal experience may have been largely based on polder reclamation he must have been versed in the writings and works of such men as Simon Stevin, Andries Vierlingh and Leeghwater with their wider application of the principles and practice of what we should today call hydrology. With this knowledge, and putting his own particular theory into effect, he practically abandoned the northern channel of the Don passing through the hamlets of Fishlake, Sykehouse, and Snaith, to discharge into the river Aire. As later events were to prove, however sound this decision may have been in theory, it was, in fact, to constitute the ultimate, and perhaps most potent, influence in the financial failure of the whole undertaking. But it is not true to say that Vermuyden's scheme for the draining and reclamation of the Level of Hatfield was technically a failure. There were certain features of the scheme which, experience was to show, might have been treated differently. That is merely being wise after the event. To say that it was a financial failure for the participants as a whole is to state a fact. That, however, is not necessarily an indictment against Vermuyden. Nobody could have expected him, or anybody else, to foresee all the difficulties with which the undertaking was to be faced, the legal disputes over rights of common, and the intense antagonism of the local inhabitants against the foreigners. In 1626 the hopes of all were high and on the day on which the agreement between King Charles and Vermuyden was signed, 24th May, the Privy Council issued:

'A passe for Cornelius Vermuyden to repaire into the Lowe Countries and to take with him his wife, 2 children, 2 men-servants and 2 maide servantes and such necessary provisions, not prohibited, as they shall have occastion to use.'[1]

And no doubt on his arrival in the Netherlands he had a heartening story to tell to the van Valckenburghs, the van Peenens, Philibert Vernatti, Johan Corsellis, Cornelius van Beuren, Pieter Cruyspenninck, Leonard and Jacob Cats, and all his other fellow participants who were adventuring their money in the undertaking.

[1] *Acts of the Privy Council.* March, 1626 to May, 1626. p. 486.

CHAPTER FIVE

Difficulties in the Hatfield Chase undertaking. Vermuyden's knighthood. Appointment as Director of Works for draining Great Level.

ANY attempt to compress the complicated story of the initial drainage undertaking in Hatfield Chase into a few pages would be an attempt at the impossible. For those who desire to study the subject in detail there are the three earlier descriptions of Hunter, Stonehouse and Tomlinson,[1] and even if due regard is paid to the partisan feelings of these three writers, and allowances made for some historical inaccuracies, there will evolve from their books at least an indication of how complicated the story is. The later, and, perhaps, more accurate, description of Korthals Altes[2] will confirm this indication. But it must be emphasised that the complications do not arise primarily from technical considerations. While, undoubtedly, it is true to say that there were faults, real or imaginary, in Vermuyden's scheme, and while, consequently, there were complaints against the inadequacy of the measures which he had adopted in order to achieve the object of making land fit for 'tillage and pasture', there has never been the same continuing argument and discussion over the technical principles employed in Hatfield Chase such as have persisted for centuries over the work of Vermuyden in the Great Level. It is true, of course, that the limited area of the Chase has depreciated its importance, an importance later overshadowed by the wider 'adventure' of the Great Level, but in the years immediately following 1626 Hatfield Chase was the largest reclamation scheme undertaken in England up to that time and with it were created all the difficulties inherent in its novelty, difficulties which were increased particularly by its almost completely foreign domination. This alien influence was not confined to the indirect one of finance only. Vermuyden himself, so active personally in the Level during the early years of the work, was still considered a foreigner in spite of the fact that he and his wife had

[1] JOSEPH HUNTER, *op. cit.* W. B. STONEHOUSE, *op. cit.* J. TOMLINSON, *The Level of Hatfield Chase*, 1882.

[2] J. KORTHALS ALTES, *op. cit.*

taken the precaution in 1624 of being naturalised, and at the commencement of the undertaking, shortly after Vermuyden's visit to the Netherlands in 1626, an army of Netherlanders descended on the Level to implement the scheme which he had evolved. That their arrival was looked upon by the local inhabitants with more than disfavour is understandable. A natural distaste for foreigners was aggravated by an insularity arising from the seclusion of the country of Hatfield Chase. In addition, there was a strong objection to any form of drainage and reclamation whether by foreigners or by their own countrymen, and while, generally speaking, there was at first little, if any, physical obstruction to the new work, there was, on the whole only a sullen acquiescence to a thoroughly unpopular state of affairs. That, however, was only one aspect of the matter, and important though it was to prove, the rock on which the participants were eventually to founder was mainly the legal one concerned with the rights of common, and leading to interminable lawsuits, injunctions and other legal processes. All, therefore, it will be possible to do here will be to give an outline picture of how all this was to affect Vermuyden personally, and his future career.

The expedition with which the work on the scheme went forward was truly remarkable, and certainly a tribute to the organising ability and energy of Vermuyden himself. In about eighteen months from the signing of the original agreement, towards the end of 1627, Vermuyden was able to claim that the work was completed and to make application for the appointment of the Commission to survey and allot the reclaimed lands. This Commission, consisting of Viscount Aire, a son-in-law of Sir Robert Swift, Sir John Saville, Sir Ralph Hansby and Sir Thomas Fanshaw, commenced its labour in 1628 and at once came up against clear evidence of the dissatisfaction of the local inhabitants both with the results of the drainage scheme itself, and with what were considered injustices in the destruction of the rights of the commoners. And thus began the long and tedious legal battle.

Dealing first with the technical aspects of the matter, and the complaints against the results, or lack of results, achieved by the scheme, it can be said that Vermuyden's principle of replacing the tortuous natural channels of rivers by artificial straight cuts was fundamentally and theoretically sound. Similarly the principle of concentrating the waters of the Don in one channel had everything to recommend it except the fact that the one channel employed was not large enough to deal with the waters hitherto flowing in three. It was, incidentally, on this one northern channel that the utilisation of 'washes' was effected, the southern bank of the river being placed some distance back from the river bed so that the land between the river and the bank could be used, as the agreement stipulated, as receptacles 'of the sudden downfall of water'. Nobody criticised Vermuyden's 'washes' in Hatfield Chase, but the inhabitants of the villages of Fishlake, Sykehouse and Snaith, more interested in results than in principles, complained bitterly that their lands, hitherto free from floodings, were now inundated by water from the one remaining channel of the Don, inadequate to deal with all the water flowing to it. There was no denying that Vermuyden's scheme had on the whole immensely benefitted the Level and had successfully converted a large acreage of marsh land into land fit for tillage and pasture. But at the same time certain areas of land, not solely those of Fishlake, Sykehouse, and Snaith, had been adversely affected and the inhabitants of those areas had just ground for complaint. That was one side of the picture. But there was another, and, perhaps, more serious problem, the rights of the commoners.

The agreement between Charles and Vermuyden had recognised the existence of rights of common and had specifically stated that Vermuyden should begin work three months after the King had come to an agreement 'with such person or persons as have claim to drain any estate, interest, or common of or in the said grounds'. The reaching of such an agreement by the King might have been a comparatively simple matter if the 'grounds' included in the agreement had consisted only of Hatfield Chase itself. The Chase was Crown land on which the inhabitants were solely tenants or copyholders possessing legally no rights of common except certain privileges of cutting turves anciently granted to the Abbey of Selby and transferred to the inhabitants of Crowle. But in the adjoining area of the Isle of Axholme the inhabitants possessed undoubted common rights secured to them by a deed of Sir John Mowbray, executed in 1359 in the reign of Edward III. The Crown, therefore, was in no position to allot or assign any commons without specific agreement on the part of the commoners. The Attorney-General, Sir Robert Heath, must have been aware of this state of affairs and, being so closely associated with Vermuyden, should have warned him of the danger. Perhaps he did and yet in spite of this Vermuyden failed to realise the extent to which this question could affect the undertaking, and thus impetuously he set the work in hand before Charles had reached agreement with the commoners. The resulting costly litigation itself nearly ruined the undertaking while at the same time the workmen of the undertaking were meeting with constant obstruction, and destruction of embankments, until organised rioting on the inhabitants reached such a pitch as sometimes to result in loss of life. This rioting was not merely the spontaneous demonstration of the antagonism of the commoners. It had behind it also the support of some of the wealthier landowners, but in spite of this state of affairs, it was still possible for Vermuyden to claim at the end of 1627 that the drainage was completed.

The year 1628 saw an increase in the intensity of the rioting and, for example, on 21 August of that year a correspondent was writing to George Villiers, Duke of Buckingham, telling him of how in a clash between 'Mr. Vermuyden's friends and workmen and the people of the Isle of Axholme', a man had been killed by the Dutch party and expressing the opinion that the killing of this man was 'conceived to be murder in all who gave directions to go armed that day'. The letter went on to say that 'these outrages will produce good effects. They will procure conformity in the people, and enforce Vermuyden to sue for favour at the Duke's hands—if not for himself, for divers of his friends.'[1]

The meaning of this last sentence is somewhat obscure, but apparently refers to efforts which the Duke of Buckingham had made to purchase for himself some of the lands of the Level of Hatfield either from Vermuyden, or from others of the participants, but without success. The hope was that the riotous opposition of the inhabitants would induce the participants to part with some of their lands, a state of affairs which in time came to pass, but in August 1628, Vermuyden, the Vernattis, the van Valckenburghs and the rest still looked upon the undertaking as a profitable speculation and had no intention of relinquishing their profits to anyone, even such an exalted personage as George Villiers. In actual fact the Duke never received this letter as on the day following that on which it was written he was assassinated by Felton at Portsmouth.

It was easy to condemn Vermuyden and his workmen for going armed against the riotous inhabitants, but continual provocation and wanton destruction of the drainage works by riotous bands called for drastic measures. In July 1628, Vermuyden had purchased the manors of Hatfield, Fishlake, Thorne, Stainforth and Dowsthorpe from the King for the sum of £10,000, at a yearly rent of £195 3s. 2½d. with an improved rent of £425, and therefore, his title to these lands was a perfectly good one even if the passing of the lordship of these manors into the hands of a foreigner, naturalised though he might be, did nothing to diminish the unpopularity of Vermuyden. Rioting continued throughout most of 1628 and reached such a pitch that on 28th September, the Privy Council felt compelled to issue an order from Hampton Court to the Attorney-General, Sir Robert Heath, telling him that he 'should make ready a proclamation forbidding the inhabitants of the Isle of Axholme to oppose the works that Mr. Vermuyden had in hand, for draining the waste and drowned lands of the cos.

[1] *Cal. State Paper Dom. Charles I.* Vol. CXIII. 38.

of York, Lincoln, and Nottingham.'[1] Sir Robert Heath was prompt in taking the necessary steps, with some effect too, for in October Sir Philibert Vernatti was writing to a friend telling him that he had recently been down to inspect the drainage work which was going on at Haxey and that 'the mutinous people have not only desisted from their threats, but now give their work to complete the dike, which they have fifty times destroyed and thrown into the river. A royal proclamation made by a sergeant-at-arms in their village, accompanied by the sheriff and other officials, with 50 horsemen, and an exhortation mingled with threats of fire and vengeance, have produced this result'.[2]

On 6th January, 1628-9 Charles, with all due ceremony, at Whitehall conferred the honour of knighthood on Cornelius Vermuyden and even if it is admitted that by that time the work which he had carried out at Hatfield had accomplished much towards the 'laying dry' of the drowned lands, it is also clear that the task was far from being complete, as the future was to show. Perhaps therefore, excessive cynicism is not necessary to see the knighthood not solely as the reward for the benefits of the drainage but as some return for the money which Vermuyden had directed into the pocket of Charles. Not that Charles was to benefit personally by the sale of Hatfield Manor because the sum of £10,000 was handed over to Sir Sackville Crow, Treasurer of the Navy and in July 1629, Charles instructed Lord Treasurer Weston that the improved rent of £425, together with that of £60 for lands at Wroote in Lincolnshire, also purchased by Vermuyden, should be granted to the Dowager Duchess of Buckingham and Sir George Manners 'for the use of the new Duke of Buckingham, for the payment of the late Duke's debts, or for the preferment of her other children unprovided for.'[1] A touching tribute to the memory of one whose death had been a very bitter blow to Charles.

During all this time matters were becoming more difficult and complicated for Vermuyden and for the participants in general in spite of the fact that the Commission under Viscount Aire had duly allotted to the adventurers their one third share of the land recovered in the Level. This fact, had, indeed, complicated matters still further for the reason that there was an outcry on the part of the local inhabitants against the award of the Commission and an accusation that the most profitable lands had been allotted solely to the participants. At the same time the inhabitants of Fishlake, Sykehouse and Snaith continued strongly to protest against the flooding of their lands owing to the overflowing of the Don. Vermuyden's contention

[1] *Cal. State Paper Dom. Charles I.* Vol. CXVII. 75.

[2] *Cal. State Paper. Dom. Charles I.* Vol. CXIX. 73.

on this point was that the flooding was due primarily to the failure of these towns to keep the banks in a state of repair, a contention which for the time being was accepted by the authorities to whom the protests were made. But as time went on and the flooding continued it became obvious that the trouble was seated deeper than in faulty repairs to the banks. It was also eventually realised that here existed one of the faults in Vermuyden's scheme and that even if he was right in his principle of concentrating the waters of the Don in one channel, that channel should have been provided with a direct outfall into the River Ouse and not into the Aire. But it was not until the year 1633 that Thomas Wentworth, later Earl of Strafford, then President of the Council of the North, gave judgement in the suit which compelled the Participants to cut an entirely new channel from Turnbridge to Goole by which the waters of the Don were conveyed direct to the Ouse at the latter place. This channel, still to this day known as the Dutch River, was the last nail in the coffin of the Participants' hopes. Their finances already strained to breaking-point could stand no more and the sum of £20,000, the cost of the new channel, was the last straw too heavy for them to carry. There was not, of course, a sudden collapse of the adventure but gradually the participants began to realise that all they could look forward to was a constant drain on their resources. Vermuyden gradually disposed of all his interest in the Level of Hatfield, but he was not numbered among those who returned disillusioned to their native land. And he was far from being penniless. In the year 1630 he had purchased from the Crown 4,000 acres of land in Sedgmoor in Somerset for £12,000, and Malvern Chase in Worcestershire for £5,000. In the same year he was engaged by Francis, 4th Earl of Bedford, as engineer or director for the drainage of the Great Level of the Fens. His feet were on the pathway of twenty-five years of stormy struggle to end in remarkable achievement.

CHAPTER SIX

Assessment of results in Hatfield Chase. Vermuyden's relations with Wentworth and Sir Robert Heath.

IT must be emphasised again that technically the Hatfield Chase undertaking was not a failure. Faults it undoubtedly possessed, faults due to mistakes in anticipation on Vermuyden's part. But those faults were of a comparatively minor nature and even if they were seized upon and exaggerated by Vermuyden's enemies it would have been impossible to deny that the state of the Level was infinitely improved on the completion of the work. The whole face of the Level had been changed from continuous swamp to arable and grazing lands, subject, it is true, in some cases to periodic flooding, but, generally speaking, land fit for tillage and pasture. The cost of cutting the Dutch River may have been the last straw in bringing about the financial collapse of the original undertaking, but it must also be emphasised that this was so only because the undertaking had been so enfeebled by the constant opposition of, and damage by, the local inhabitants, and the complicated and costly legal difficulties of ownerships, tenants, common rights, scots and so on. The terms of the original agreement between Charles and Vermuyden should have guarded against all these legal difficulties with their consequent crippling impositions and it can be wondered how much Charles is to be blamed for the failure of the undertaking by his own failure to come to terms with the inhabitants before the undertakers commenced work. The original agreement was between Vermuyden and the King and Vermuyden's was the genius which devised the scheme and guided it through all its vicissitudes to the depressing end. Vermuyden was the dominant figure in the enterprise and it was to him that all the discredit was given while his fellow participants sat quietly in the background content to let the odium which the scheme generated be heaped on the head of Vermuyden. Not that Vermuyden objected to this. His was a masterful personality prepared to bear any consequences. Not in any spirit of meekness, but as a fighter ready to give as much as he received, and more. Often tactless, always resourceful and replete with energy and, it might appear, generally concerned more with the interests of Cornelius Vermuyden than with those of his fellow participants.

One of the most striking features of the career of Vermuyden is the position which he gained for himself in Court circles and the patronage which he secured from the two Kings, James and Charles. No doubt this favour in Court circles was not an unmixed blessing and may have been the cause of the apparent antagonism of Buckingham, and it is an interesting speculation to wonder what effect this might have had on Vermuyden's future had Felton not struck that fatal blow at Portsmouth. That Vermuyden and Thomas Wentworth did not always see eye to eye is understandable since Wentworth in his official capacity had often to give verdicts against the Participants and in favour of the inhabitants of the Level. Not that these judgements were anything but legally sound but Vermuyden's refusal to accept them and to carry out their provisions did nothing to improve relations between the two men. Vermuyden could not have known the power to which Wentworth was to rise, but it is to the latter's credit that there is no evidence to show that he in any way attempted to hinder Vermuyden in his later ventures before he himself was sacrificed on the scaffold in 1641. It was in November 1628, that Sir Philibert Vernatti in writing to his friend, the Rev. Mr. Squires, told him, among other things, that on some unspecified occasion 'the King publicly thanked Mr. Verm[uyden] for his services done to him and the country, and openly rebuked Lord Wentworth and Sir Ralph Hanby'.[1] The reason for the rebuke is not given. It may have been on account of the continuance of rioting against Vermuyden and his workmen, but it can be imagined that a public rebuke of this nature did not make for more cordial feelings on the part of Wentworth.

In August of the following year Wentworth had occasion to write to the Privy Council from Wentworth Woodhouse and to point out that he, as Lord President of the Council of the North had been instructed to suppress some supposed revolt near Hatfield Chase against the work of Sir Cornelius Vermuyden, but that, in fact, no such disturbances had occurred. If, therefore, he wrote, Sir Cornelius has informed any such thing 'he has abused the Council with an untruth and deserves reprehension.'[2] Thus it will be seen from these two typical incidents that the tension between Vermuyden and Wentworth was gradually mounting. Unfortunately for Vermuyden, Wentworth had the law on his side and Court favour had no influence on the able Lord President of the Council of the North. Even if the judgements

[1] *Cal. State Paper Dom. Charles I.* Vol. CXIX. 45.
[2] *Ibid.* Vol. CXLVIII. 42.

given against him in the claims by the commoners did not always seem just, Vermuyden was faced by a stronger opponent than he appeared sometimes to realise. Refusal to abide by these judgements could only lead to one end. Doubtless Sir Robert Heath did his best in the interests of Vermuyden as is evidenced by his letter of May 1632, to Sir John Coke, then Principal Secretary to the King, telling him of the difficulties which Vermuyden was encountering in obtaining recognition of his title to the lands of Malvern Chase, purchased in 1630.[1] But a year later, in June 1633, Francis, Lord Cottingham, was also writing to Coke telling him that 'Vermuyden is yet a prisoner by commandment of the Lords for having refused to contribute towards that new work the proportion which their Lords have ordained',[2] meaning by the 'new work' the construction of the Dutch River, judgement for which work having been given earlier in the year by the Court presided over by Wentworth.

Vermuyden in the end had to bow to the inevitable and pay his contribution, but on his release from his confinement he gave no indication of being in any more chastened mood. In the month following the imprisonment one Hugh Speyring related that when he had asked Vermuyden how the suit between him and the participants was proceeding in Chancery, 'he scoffingly answered that it would be time enough seven years hence to ask that question, and further that the Lords of the Council were ashamed of the orders which they had made concerning his imprisonment, and did not know how with credit to get off from what they had done.'[3]

All these happenings were long after Vermuyden had, as far as possible, shaken the soil of Hatfield Chase off his feet. He had disposed of most of his interests there, but, unfortunately for him, not of all his liabilities, and was engaged in the larger work of the Great Level. He had quarrelled with a number of his fellow participants in Hatfield Chase, and was involved in legal suits with them. Many of the participants had reaped no reward from the venture and while it would be untrue to attribute this situation personally to Vermuyden it is impossible to overlook the fact that, in spite of all the vicissitudes through which the undertaking struggled to financial failure, Vermuyden himself emerged with his ownership of 4,000 acres of Sedgmoor, not worth much, perhaps in their undrained state but the result of a payment of £12,000 to the Crown; his temporary ownership of Malvern Chase;[4] his partnership with Sir Robert Heath in the lead mines at Wirksworth; a

[1] *H.M.C. 12th Report.* App. Part I Vol. I. 457. (Coke MSS).
[2] *Ibid.* Part II Vol. II. 17.
[3] *Cal. State Paper Dom. Charles I.* Vol. CCXLIII. 65
[4] See pp. 117-118 *infra.*

knighthood; and his appointment as engineer for the draining of the 300,000 acres of the Great Level of the Fens.

It is easy to ascribe the personal success of Vermuyden during the first dozen years or so of his career in England to Court favour. No doubt this was a strong influence, but there was more behind it than that alone. Vermuyden had ability of two kinds. He knew where and how to make, and to use, his friends, and he possessed the technical ability which, for the class of work which he undertook, had to be a combination of a capacity to appreciate a situation and administrative skill to carry through a scheme to a practical conclusion. Let us, for the moment forget the Dagenham episode and the failure which it appeared to be. The Hatfield Chase undertaking was not, as we must repeat, a failure technically even if it was not perfect, and in passing it might be said that no Fen drainage or reclamation scheme in this country has ever been unanimously considered to be a full success. But right or wrong, the organisation required to see the undertaking through from the financial preliminaries to its conclusion was a task worthy of a man of energy, foresight and intelligence. It is debatable whether Vermuyden could be considered to have been a likeable man, and doubtless he had no desire to be so considered. If a seventeenth-century portrait can provide a basis on which to judge the subject's character, this material is at hand because there is in the possession of the writer a portrait of Vermuyden by the Dutch painter van Miereveld, the only known portrait of Vermuyden extant.[1] The date on which it was painted is not known, but this is considered likely to be round about 1638 when Vermuyden was in the full favour of Charles I, and certainly it must have been painted before 1641 the year in which van Miereveld died. The portrait belonged originally to Col. Maurice Noel, through whose generosity it came into the writer's possession, and formed part of a large collection of contemporary portraits of many of the participants in the Hatfield Chase undertaking, Philibert Vernatti, Gabriel Vernatti, the van Valckenburghs, Johan Corsellis, Samuel van Peene, and others, Col. Noel being a direct descendant through the Earls of Gainsborough of the second creation of Anna Margaretta Vernatti, great-grand-daughter of Gabriel Vernatti. From this portrait a strong, determined face looks down with something of arrogance and a contempt for weaker mortals, the face of a man who knew what he wanted, and was prepared to sacrifice anything, except his own interests, to get it.

But any judgement on the character of Vermuyden made at this stage must be founded on the evidence of the Hatfield undertaking, evidence very limited in quantity and, certainly, one-sided in quality. In the year 1630

[1] See Appendix, p. 161.

the great adventure, using the word in its modern sense, of the Great Level of the Fens lay before him, an adventure which was to span twenty-five years of one of the most turbulent periods in the history of England. At the end of those twenty-five years it will be time to weigh up once more the evidence which they provide, bearing in mind, however, that in judging the character of an individual of the seventeenth century by his publicly proclaimed actions, and the criticisms of those actions, it is as well to remember, firstly, that at that time the law of libel was somewhat leniently interpreted and secondly, that standards of honesty were very different from those of today. That Vermuyden was ruthless, that he was unscrupulous, is a likely conclusion, a conclusion perhaps borne out by the following incident which, if it is quoted somewhat out of its context, does arise from his original friendship and association with Sir Robert Heath dating back to the early days of the Hatfield undertaking.

Heath undoubtedly was an extremely useful friend to Vermuyden. He had helped to maintain Charles's interest in the subject of fen drainage, he had interceded on Vermuyden's behalf in the matter of Malvern Chase. In September 1633, he was writing again to Sir John Coke telling him that 'since your going into Scotland Sir Cornelius Vermuyden has been pursued by his adversary at the Council Board, and hath fallen out unreasonably for our mines in Derbyshire where he should have been long since'.[1] The unnamed 'adversary' was, presumably, Wentworth. Heath and Vermuyden were at this time associated in the venture of the lead mines at Wirksworth and doubtless the former was on this occasion concerned principally with his own interest there, but clearly, whatever his motives, his friendship had a very definite value to Vermuyden. And yet, to anticipate some twenty years, Vermuyden was prepared to jettison any loyalty to that friendship in his own interests. Heath was a staunch Royalist. He followed Charles to Oxford and eventually became Chief Justice of King's Bench. On the defeat of the King and his execution in 1649, Parliament exempted Heath from pardon and he fled to France, dying in Calais in 1652. In July of that year his son and heir was petitioning the Committee for Compounding asserting that Cornelius Vermuyden was denying the petitioner's title to the mine and was claiming the whole property for himself.[2] It is not suggested that this isolated incident can be considered as a basis for a judgement on, or condemnation of, Vermuyden's character as a whole, but it is to be feared that it does give some indication of his general course of conduct. Or is that, perhaps too harsh a generalisation

[1] *H.M.C., 12th Report*, Appendix, Vol. II, p. 29.

[2] *Proc. of the Committee of Compounding with Delinquents, 1643–1660*, Part IV, 2775.

CHAPTER SEVEN

The Great Level. Early proposals by Ayloffe and Thomas, and others. Privy Council's abortive negotiations with Vermuyden in 1630. Contract with Francis, Earl of Bedford. Vermuyden's plans and progress. Charles I becomes 'undertaker.'

THE year 1630 was to be a momentous one for Sir Cornelius Vermuyden and for the Great Level of the Fens. As has been said earlier, it was not long after the so-called completion of the Hatfield Chase undertaking that Vermuyden began gradually to dispose of his possessions there, and soon after 1630 he sold all his interest in the manor of Hatfield to John Gibbons, the property a short time after this passing into the ownership of Sir Arthur Ingram. Tradition has it that Sir Cornelius built himself a house in the Level of Hatfield, and, indeed, there is a house in the neighbourhood of Epworth still pointed out as having been his. There is nothing contradictory in the supposition that he did build such a house, but so far no documentary evidence in proof has been produced. There are other houses, one in Fen Drayton in Cambridgeshire, and one in Highbridge in Somerset, to both of which the story of ownership by Sir Cornelius Vermuyden is attached. All these houses have this in common. Their architecture is distinctly Dutch in character, but it has not yet been possible to prove that Vermuyden either built or owned them, although, again, the supposition, and tradition, is not unreasonable. Certainly the Vermuydens were established in London by the year 1630. Their first child, a daughter Sarah, may have been born there, or possibly in Holland, in the year 1624, but no trace of registration of her birth or baptism has yet been discovered in England. The eldest son, Cornelius, was baptised at St. Botolph's, Bishopgate, on 19th March, 1626, and may have been born in 1625. A third child, Catherine, was baptised at the Dutch Reformed Church, Austin Friars, on 22nd January, 1626–7, to be followed by two sons Thomas and John, both baptised at St. Dionys Backchurch in the city, but a general discussion on the children of Sir Cornelius and Lady Katherine must be deferred until a later period of this book.

When the proposal of Cornelius Liens and Cornelius Vermuyden for the drainage of the Great Level had been rejected in 1622, in spite of the distractions of Hatfield Chase and his other smaller enterprises Sir Cornelius had certainly not dismissed the Great Level from his mind. Nor, it must be assumed, had his associates in the Netherlands. By the same token, there were many ambitious individuals in England who were still anxious and willing to 'adventure' their money on the project. Vermuyden was fully aware of this and he also realised that his most dangerous competitor was Sir Anthony Thomas (he had been knighted on 5th September, 1619) who had now been joined by John Worsopp, Henry Briggs the mathematician, and more famous for his logarithms, Hildebrand Prusen, 'citizen and salter of London', Cornelius Drible, that inventive genius from the Netherlands and the constructor of the first submarine,[1] and others. Thomas was in close touch with the King on whose instructions the Commissioners of Sewers met him in Cambridge on 1st October, 1629, and requested him to demonstrate to them the plan by which he proposed to effect his drainage scheme. But Sir Anthony, either not ready with his scheme or wanting to make sure of his profit before disclosing his methods, refused to do this until the Commissioners had agreed to set a tax of 10 shillings on every acre. The Commissioners on their part refused to do anything of the kind, pointing out that this would mean a charge of £150,000, a sum which they considered absolutely unreasonable and beyond their powers to agree to. Furthermore, they pointed out that they had received an offer for the carrying out of the work for £35,000.[2] Sir Anthony and his fellow adventurers do not, on the face of it, appear to have had a very straight deal. Whatever may have been the powers of the Commissioners to raise the sum of £150,000, the fact remains that this sum, as events were to prove, would have been totally inadequare as should at that stage have been apparent when the minor operations in Hatfield Chase were said to have cost £200,000, even if this was a slight exaggeration.

At this stage the Privy Council turned to Sir Cornelius Vermuyden. At least, that must be the conclusion because there is no available evidence to show that Vermuyden himself approached the Council although, doubtless, he was fully aware of the course of events and was forwarding his own interests in a rather less conspicuous manner. It must be remembered that at that time he was a man of some reputation and that the full implications of the Hatfield Chase undertaking had not then come to light. Added to which, of course, were the close relations which he had with Charles. And

[1] Tierie Gerrit, *Cornelius Drebble (1572–1633)*, Paris 1932.

[2] *Cal. State Papers Domestic, Charles I*, Vol. CL. 2, p. 69.

thus it was that some time towards the end of 1629, on 1st September to be exact, a contract was made with Cornelius Vermuyden for the draining of the Level. There is, unfortunately, a somewhat curious lack of exact information on this phase of the negotiations and it has not been possible to find any definite reference to an agreement, written or otherwise, in the State Papers of the period. Dugdale himself is extremely vague on the matter confining himself to a mere statement that such an agreement was entered into 'with Sir Cornelius Vermuden [*sic*] (a person well experienced in works of this kind)' and adding that Vermuyden's recompence was to be '95,000 acres of the said surrounded lands'.[1] If an agreement was made, and it has always been accepted that such was the case, although we know, that it was not proceeded with, there are two points which are open to much discussion. Firstly, there is evidence to make it open to doubt whether the recompense offered was not 95,000 acres but 90,000, and secondly, there is the inevitable question of where the finance was coming from. Certainly one cannot believe that Vermuyden was possessed of sufficient resources of his own and, therefore, the conclusion must be that he had made arrangements, or hoped to make arrangements, to enlist the support of his friends in the Netherlands. There is, however, no evidence to support such a conclusion which can only be based on assumption.

The reason usually given for the fact that the contract with Vermuyden was never proceeded with is that the outcry against the undertaking being entrusted to a foreigner was so great that the Commissioners of Sewers withdrew from the proposal and assented to the making of a contract with the Earl of Bedford. There may be something in this, but it is felt that the breakdown of negotiations with Vermuyden was not solely due to objections to his alien ancestry—he had, indeed, been naturalised six years previously—but largely to his refusal to accept what he considered the inadequate recompense of 90,000 acres when he had stipulated that this should be 95,000 acres, the acreage which was later given to the Earl of Bedford. Further comment on this is unneccessary except to emphasise that, as was to become clear in later years, considerable pressure was required to make Vermuyden compromise on any carefully calculated demand which he had made.

Before, however, we go on to relate the story of the Earl of Bedford's undertaking, in order to have a clearer understanding of the situation at that period, it will be necessary to return to Sir Anthony Thomas. Prior to the time of the making of the agreement with Vermuyden in September 1630, and that with the Earl of Bedford in January 1630–31 Thomas and his associates published on 11th January, 1629–30 'The Propositions of Sir

[1] Dugdale, *op. cit.*, p. 408.

Anthony Thomas, and John Worsop Esquire, for making of the bargaine with the Country . . . for the drayning of the Levell . . .'[1] thus showing that they were still prepared to carry on the fight. This document contains some interesting, not to say illuminating information. In the first place reference is made to an offer which apparently had been made to 'Master Burrell and His Associates, for the drayning of the great Levell' for which they were to be allotted 80,000 acres out of which the undertakers agreed to 'ingage . . . 10,000 acres for the maintenance of the worke'. That is all we know of this proposal, but we shall later on become acquainted with another member of the Burrell family. Thomas and his friends said that if the 80,000 acres were allotted to them they were prepared to 'ingage 15,000 Acres, and a rent of 4d the Acre out of the whole 80,000 Acres amounting to 1333 l per annum, for the maintenance of our worke, and will give to every Cottager, whose house shall happen to stand upon any part of the Land allotted to us, the summe of four pounds towards the erecting of a new house, in some other part of the Common'.

These terms were very different from those which had been demanded in the previous October, but the main points for comment are the accusations contained in the document of bad faith on the parts of both James I and Charles I. Referring to Thomas's original proposal in company with Sir William Ayloffe of 1618, it was stated that when James had ordered the Council to come to terms with the applicants, the Council had instructed Ayloffe and Thomas to present a Bill to Parliament and they had engaged one 'Mr. Crooke, then a Barrester of Greys Inne' to draw up the Bill. Parliament was shortly after this dissolved and nothing done on the Bill but subsequently when James declared himself the undertaker he had promised to pay to Sir Anthony Thomas 'a reward of Ten thousand pounds, for his great travell and charge therein'. Thus the matter rested until 1629 when in February of that year Sir Anthony made another application to proceed with an undertaking and on 16th June received a letter[2] from Charles which gave the impression that he was prepared to view their application with favour. But by this time Sir Thomas Crooke (he had been created a baronet in Ireland) had allied himself with William Burrell, and using all the confidential information acquired when in the employ of Sir Anthony, had made proposals of his own to the Council for draining the Great Level for the sum of £35,000, the sum mentioned by the Commissioners in their communication of 1st October 1629. And, of course, Thomas had by then seen nothing of the promised £10,000. Nor was he ever destined to do so.

[1] *State Papers Domestic, Charles I* (S.P. 16) Vol. 158, No. 34.
[2] *Cal. State Papers Domestic, Charles I*, Vol. CXLIV, p. 579, 84.

Accepting all these accusations at their face value, the whole matter has a very unsavoury flavour, and when the negotiations which had been proceeding with Sir Cornelius Vermuyden broke down and 'the country . . . became humble suitors to Francis then Earl of Bedford . . . to undertake the work',[1] Sir Anthony Thomas and his friends certainly had some justification for feeling that they had had a raw deal and that favour at Court was a very potent factor in the Great Level of the Fens.

Francis, fourth Earl of Bedford, was possessed of all the shrewdness inherited from his ancestor, John Russell, the first Earl, coupled with the energy of his distinguished father, William, Baron Russell of Thornhaugh. When he decided to take an active part in the drainage of the Great Level it may be true, if somewhat misleading, to say that 'he gave his thoughts to an undertaking highly patriotic in its principle, and vast in its design'.[2] There is no denying that the undertaking could have been highly patriotic in principle and was certainly vast in design, but that does not necessarily imply that patriotic motives occupied any conspicuous place in the Earl's thoughts, or for that matter, any place at all. The Earl was interested in the drainage of the Great Level for two practical reasons. Firstly, he possessed, as we know, an extensive tract of the Level in his Thorney estate, and, secondly, apart from any direct advantage to this estate itself, he saw the undertaking as a profitable investment for his money. Nor could he be blamed for either of these points of view. The Earl's intervention had undoubtedly saved the enterprise from again collapsing as it had so often in the past, but Wells's statement that 'a more striking instance of self-devotion to the wishes of the people, and the real benefit of the state, appears not upon the records of history',[3] will be appreciated more truly when it is realised that when it was written in 1830 Wells was employed as Register of the Corporation of the Bedford Level and John, Duke of Bedford, was the Governor of the Corporation. A more honest comment on the matter is contained in a letter written by Francis himself from Woburn in July 1630 to Sir Henry Vane, Ambassador at the Hague in which he tells him that the 'Fen business is so feasible, and may be so profitable . . . that the Earl is very willing to force Sir Henry into the adventure'. He says that he is going to venture some of his own 'shrunk fortune, and expects some person of quality and judgement to be there from Sir Henry to join with Vermuyden, by the 14th August'.[4]

[1] DUGDALE, *op. cit.*, p. 408.
[2] J. H. WIFFEN, *Memoirs of the House of Russell*, 1833, Vol. II, p. 149.
[3] *History of the Bedford Level.* Vol. I., p. 106.
[4] *Cal. State Papers Domestic, Charles I*, Vol. CLXXI. 30.

The suggestion 'to join with Vermuyden' raises a speculation of some interest. The Earl of Bedford had consented to become principal undertaker in the drainage scheme, in partnership with thirteen co-adventurers, under the Lynn Law of January 1630, and in the following year the 'Indenture of Fourteen Parts' was drawn up specifying the partnership conditions for the adventurers. Among those adventurers we find the names of Sir Robert Heath, Sir Philibert Vernatti, to quote only two with whom we have already come into contact, and also of Sir Cornelius Vermuyden. Thus it will be seen that not only was Vermuyden to be the Director of Works, but he was also an 'adventurer' sharing in the proportion of his investment in the hazards and the profits of the undertaking. Indeed there appears to be little doubt that he was, in effect, *the* undertaker and that the Earl of Bedford, who recognised this fact, was merely a figurehead, principal undertaker in name only and in fact subordinated to the masterful personality of Vermuyden.

And, after all, the undertaking was completely dependent upon the scheme of drainage, and the manner of its execution, which had been evolved by Sir Cornelius. His was the master mind. He provided the plan, the thirteen other adventurers provided the money. If that plan failed, then they failed too.

In order to understand fully the principles upon which Vermuyden based his scheme of drainage in the Great Level, and to appreciate some of the later criticisms of that scheme, it is necessary to know something of the early natural system of drainage existing there some centuries before the year 1630. Incidentally, it is not intended to explain in any detail the problem of the drainage of the Fens except to say that, basically, it was the same as that which prevailed in Hatfield Chase. It was the problem of winding, tortuous rivers with small gradients endeavouring to find a way through a flat expanse of land to their outfalls into the Wash. In the Great Level the problem was complicated by the difficulty of keeping those outfalls clear, a fact which, as will be seen later, was to contribute greatly to the vicissitudes with which Vermuyden and the long line of engineers which came after him had to contend.

There are six rivers which contribute to the drainage of the Great Level, viz., the Nene and the Great Ouse, the Cam (or Granta), the Lark, the Little Ouse, and the Wissey, the last four all being tributaries of the Great Ouse. It will be noticed that no mention is made of the Welland, the Glen, or the Witham which are referred to in Camden's description of the Fens, as these drain the Lincolnshire Fens outside the Great Level. Now the courses of these six rivers at the time when Vermuyden first viewed the Great

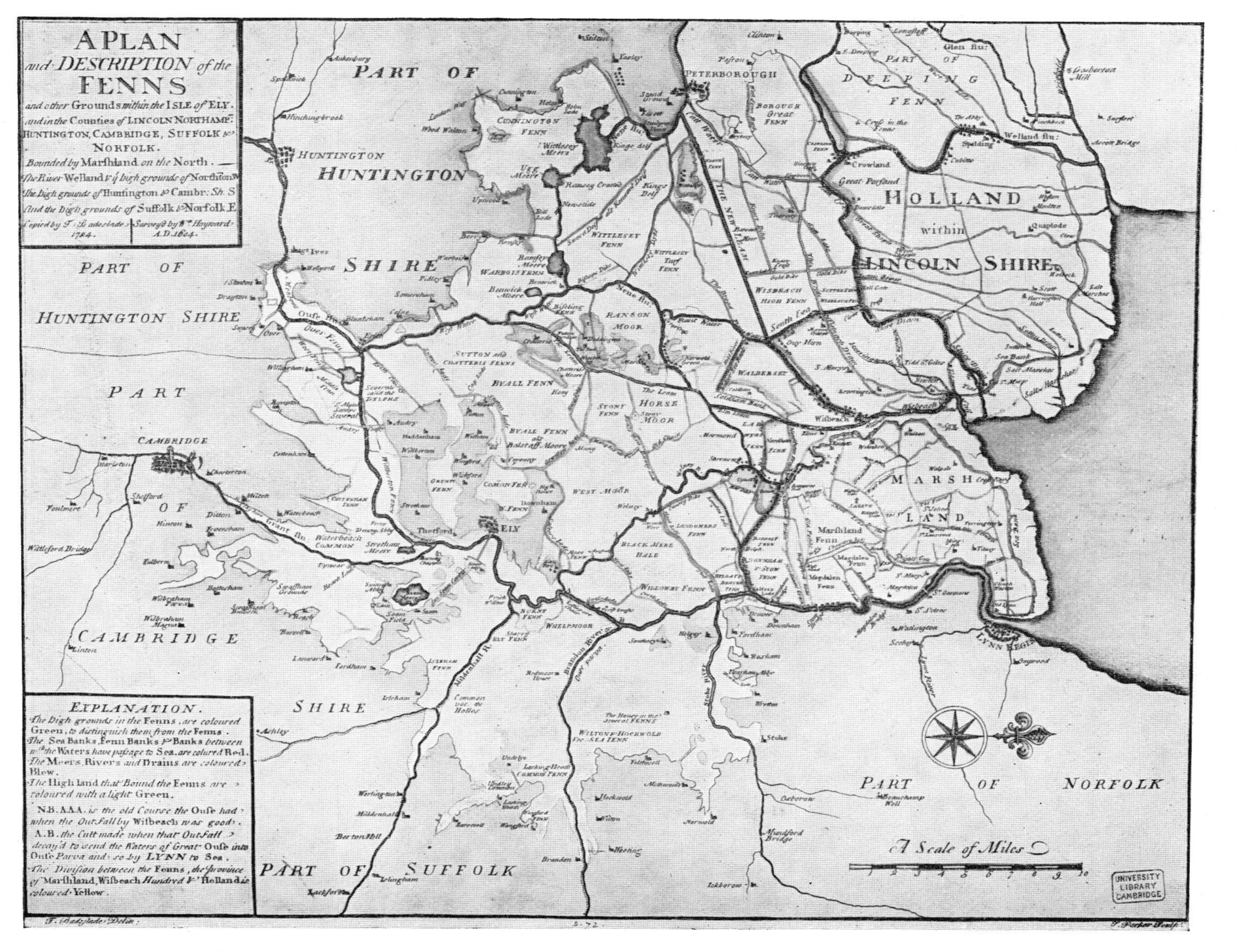

PLATE III. 'Plan and Description of the Fenns', surveyed by Hayward, 1604.
From T. Badeslade: *History of the Navigation of King's Lynn*, London, 1725.

Level were as shown in Thomas Badeslade's map of 1724 reproduced here, (Plate 3) copied from the map drawn in 1604 by William Hayward, but the situation had in fact been very different some three or four hundred years earlier.

Sometime prior to the year 1292 the Ouse, or Great Ouse as we know it today, shortly after entering the Fens at St. Ives, divided into two streams at Earith, as is shown on Badeslade's map, one, the Westwater, proceeding north to join the Nene at Benwick, the main stream following the course it does now through Ely as far as Littleport, having on its way picked up the Cam and the Lark. At Littleport it turned north-west to flow through Welney and finally to join up with the southern branch of the Nene in the neighbourhood of Upwell, and so to pass to the Wisbech outfall. The waters which flowed to King's Lynn were only those of the Little Ouse, the Wissey and the Nar, the last a small stream flowing from the uplands of Norfolk into the main stream just above King's Lynn. Indeed, at some more remote period only the Nar had flowed past King's Lynn since at that time both the Little Ouse and the Wissey had themselves joined the Nene and discharged through the Wisbech outfall.

Early in the thirteenth century serious and frequent flooding had occurred in the neighbourhood of Littleport due to the difficulty with which the waters of the Ouse and Nene forced their way through the choked outfall at Wisbech. The inhabitants of Littleport took the matter into their own hands and cut a channel to carry the waters of the Great Ouse to the Little Ouse. The consequences of this act were more decisive than they knew. In time the Great Ouse deserted its branches of the Westwater and Welney River and, taking the line of least resistance, left the Wisbech outfall and with all its tributaries, flowed, as it does today, to the Wash through King's Lynn. In other words, by the simple and local act of the inhabitants of Littleport, the whole natural system of drainage of the southern part of the Great Level was completely abandoned. It should, however, be emphasised that while the action of the inhabitants of Littleport undoubtedly precipitated this radical change it was not, in itself, the primary cause. That was the restriction of flow through the outfall of Wisbech and if the artificial cut from Littleport to Rebeck had not been made it is certain that as that outfall continued to deteriorate, the Great Ouse would eventually have found some other course to the sea, possibly through King's Lynn, but not necessarily along the channel which it now occupies.

An examination of Badeslade's map will show that at the time Vermuyden first saw the Great Level the drainage system was, to say the least, a very complicated one, bearing in some respects a similarity upon a much larger scale to the conditions which had prevailed originally in Hatfield Chase. The complexities of the several courses of the River Nene paralleled the courses of the River Don even if the attempt of Bishop Morton in the fifteenth century to improve the Nene had slightly alleviated the situation. But at Hatfield the problem had been, mainly, to get the water from the Levels into the River Trent which itself flowed into the Humber. From there, there were little further complications since the Humber had a comparatively wide and free outfall at Spurn Head. The Great Level was confined on three sides by the high ground of the counties of Northampton, Huntingdon, Cambridge, Suffolk and Norfolk, and on the fourth, or north side, it was bordered by part of Lincolnshire, the hundred of Wisbech, and that flat part of Norfolk known as Marshland. It will be seen, therefore, that the two main rivers, the Nene and the Great Ouse had several miles to travel outside the Great Level before reaching their respective outfalls below Wisbech and at King's Lynn. Furthermore it must be quite obvious that, whatever methods of internal drainage were applied, the efficiency of that method depended ultimately on the freedom of the outfalls. It is to be regretted that nothing has survived of the plan of drainage which Vermuyden had drawn up and on the basis of which he had been appointed undertaker in 1629. That such a plan was prepared is clear from the clause in the Lynn Law which states that 'Sir Cornelius Vermuyden hath, upon a map or card, described the said fenny, marsh, waste and surrounded grounds, and the outfalls thereof, by lines and other descriptions, and also writing, expressed and set down to the Commissioners of Sewers, what drains, sasses, sluices, banks, cuts and other works, he intended to make for the draining of the said surrounded grounds.'

It is impossible to say, therefore, whether in the year 1630 he realised the importance of the outfalls, or rather whether he appreciated what the state of those outfalls was at that time. But when Francis, Earl of Bedford drew up the Indenture of Fourteen Parts and agreed with his thirteen co-adventurers to become the undertakers for the drainage of the Great Level he was not content to rely solely on the plans of Vermuyden for the work. Another Dutchman, Jan Barents Westerdyke, was also invited to put forward a scheme, but whether on the comparative merits of the two schemes, or owing to the influence in Court circles which Vermuyden possessed, Westerdyke was unsuccessful in his bid for fame and retired disgruntled to his native shores. He never forgot the disappointment of his hopes and some twenty years later, as we shall see, was recalled by Francis's son William, and was able to vent some of his disapproval on Vermuyden.

The problem of the Great Level, as Vermuyden saw at first, was intimately bound up with the course of the River Great Ouse and he felt that fundamentally, whatever the vagaries of the River Nene and its several courses, and whatever subsidiary drains were cut to take the water from the surface of the Fens to the main river, as far as concerned the southern part of the Level the solution lay in augmenting the discharge capacity of the Great Ouse by providing a straight course between Earith and Denver, supplementary to the natural winding course which the river pursued between these places through Ely and Littleport. And there he cut the Bedford River 21 miles long and 70 feet wide. He also cut Bevills Leam, Sams Cut, and other minor drains but the scheme as a whole must stand or fall on the Bedford River and the principles which it incorporated irrespective of any subsequent addition of the New Bedford River some twenty years later.

The terms of the Lynn Law of 1630 under which the Earl of Bedford and his thirteen co-adventurers had become the undertakers stipulated that the recompense to the Earl on completion of the work was to be an allotment of 95,000 acres of the reclaimed land 'in free and common Soccage . . . and without paying any Rent thereto, or giving any Recompense for the same unto the King's Majesty, his Heirs or Successors, other than a Fee-Farm Rent of Ten Pounds by the year'. By the Indenture of Fourteen Parts each share was to be 7,000 acres, and, of course, the liability for the cost of the work was to be proportional to the number of shares held. The Lynn Law also stated that the work of drainage was to be completed in six years, but it is essential to note that there was no very specific stipulation of the degree to which the drainage was to be carried out. The importance of this point will become clearer later on. All that the Lynn Law said was 'That Francis Earl of Bedford would do his best endeavour at his own charge to drain the said marsh, waste, fenny and surrounding grounds, in such manner as that they shall be fit for meadow, or pasture, or arable, and it went on to make the exception that 'overflowings by sudden water which shall not lie longer upon the lands than in convenient time the same may fall away again, shall not be esteemed a not draining thereof'.

Those then were the requirements which Vermuyden was called upon to fulfil, and for which the works referred to above were designed. That they did fulfil them appeared to be proved by the Commission of Sewers which sat at St. Ives on 12th October, 1637 when it was declared that 'the Earl of Bedford had at his own costs and charges, and with the expense of great sums of money, drained the said fenny and low grounds, according to the true intent of the Lynn Law'. The Commission consequently decreed that the Earl's 95,000 acres should be set out and allotted to him, a decision which was far from being popular with the other signatories to the Indenture of Fourteen Parts who complained that Francis was gaining more than his share at their expense, threatening him with prosecution in the Star Chamber unless he treated them with more justice.'[1]

If this was true then the Earl of Bedford appears in not quite such a patriotic and magnanimous guise as Wiffen and Wells would have us believe, but more as the practical hard-headed business man that he was. Some years later, after 1649, a pamphlet was published asserting that the grant to the Earl of Bedford was entirely illegal for the reason that, while the Act of 43 Elizabeth stipulated that a lord of the manor was bound to obtain the consent of the majority of owners and commoners before commencing drainage work, this, in fact, had never been obtained although Francis had falsely stated that it had.[2] But by the year 1649, when Francis had been dead eight years, so much partisanship and politics had become intermingled with the drainage of the Great Level, that an accusation of this nature, whether true or not, was not the least unexpected.

Apart, however, from any internal disagreement among the adventurers themselves, the decision of the Commission brought a flock of petitions from, among others, the Bishop and the Dean and Chapter of Ely, and the inhabitants of Over, Willingham and Cottenham, not solely against the effectiveness, or otherwise, of the drainage measures but against the allotments which had been made to satisfy the Earl's reward of 95,000 acres. So far then it does not appear that the effectiveness of Vermuyden's scheme was questioned, but any dissatisfaction which was voiced came as well from the wealthy landowners as from the humble inhabitants who feared that they were being dispossessed unfairly of their lands. Now whatever the faults and failings of King Charles, for which in the end he was to pay so dearly, and whatever outmoded convictions of the divine right of Kings he may have held, he had many endearing qualities, not least of which was a sympathy for the rights of the oppressed where they did not conflict with those divine rights. The draining of the Great Level of the Fens, by virtue of its money-making possibilities, had become something to be influenced by politics and vested interests. In 1637 it was not, nor indeed, had it ever been that high principled and patriotic venture so beloved of Samuel Wells. But when, following the outcries against the decision of the Commission of Sewers of St. Ives, Charles himself took a hand in the game, it is doubtful whether his main object was anything but an honest desire to redress the

[1] S. R. Gardiner, *History of England*, 1884, Vol. VIII., pp. 295-299.
[2] *Ibid*, pp. 296–7. Note.

wrongs, which, quite clearly, in his opinion, had been done. With this aim in view he appointed a further Commission of Sewers to sit at Huntingdon on 12th April, 1638. Unfortunately his zeal outran his discretion and before the Commission met he rashly announced that he proposed to become the undertaker for the drainage, and practically instructed the Commissioners as to what their findings should be. There is little doubt that without any prompting from Charles the Commissioners would have reversed the decision of their predecessors at St. Ives, as indeed they did, but unfortunately for Charles he had laid himself open to the charge of prejudicing the case and precipitating a decision. This he certainly had done, but solely and honestly in his desire to see justice performed. In dealing with this episode Gardiner has quite rightly said that the story of this first attempt at draining the Great Level is worthy of attention by the historian as well as the engineer as it brings out in clear relief both the merits and defects of Charles's character.

The findings of the Commission of Huntingdon were to the effect that the Earl and his co-adventurers had not performed their contract, that the work which had been done was incomplete and defective, that the adventurers were not entitled to their recompense, and that His Majesty the King would take over the undertaking at, incidentally, an increased recompense. This decision appeared to Francis, Earl of Bedford, to have little justice as its backing, and on the face of it there seemed to be no justification for what was a high-handed act of expropriation. But a closer examination reveals a somewhat different picture.

Under the Lynn Law the Earl of Bedford and his associates were entitled to the allotment of 95,000 acres of the reclaimed land, but of this 95,000 acres only 43,000 acres were to be theirs absolutely while 12,000 were to be given to the King, and 40,000 retained as a means of providing the income for the maintenance of the drainage works. What Charles proposed when he became the undertaker was that he himself should have 152,000 acres, admittedly a somewhat regal increase, and that the Earl should be given 40,000 acres free of any liability either for maintenance or completion of the allegedly defective and uncompleted work. As at the time it was stated that the reclaimed land was worth thirty shillings an acre annually, the adventurers would, if this value were correct, obtain a yearly income of £60,000 from an expenditure which on their own showing was £100,000. A not inconsiderable return. Vermuyden may have earned the Earl's displeasure by his readiness to accept office under the usurper Charles, but it is difficult to blame him for being too practical to adopt high principles involving his own unemployment.

Thus the year 1638 saw the termination, presumably for ever, of the hopes and expectations of the adventurers and participants, and thus also, somewhat disastrously, ended the first phase of the draining of the Great Level of the Fens.

CHAPTER EIGHT

Vermuyden's 'Discourse' of 1638. Oliver Cromwell's association with the Fens and their drainage. Vermuyden's views on outfall problems. Westerdyke's divergent theories.

To what extent the work which Vermuyden had carried out by 1637 could be judged incomplete and defective depends entirely upon the interpretation of the Lynn Law and the requirements which it laid down for the drainage. From what has been quoted in the previous chapter it will be clear that those requirements were of a somewhat indeterminate nature and the stipulation that the lands should be made 'fit for meadow, or pasture, or arable' was certainly open to a very wide interpretation. This very uncertainty was probably used in 1638 as an excuse for the reversal of the decision of the Commission of 1637.

Charles, when by the adjudication of the Commission of Sewers of April 1638 he became the undertaker for the drainage, entered into his new field of activity with all the impulsive enthusiasm of which he was so well capable, but the fact that, in the end, his venture came to very little was due mainly to pressure of outside events and not to his own faults. But if little was accomplished, out of the King's undertaking came one important event.

It was only natural that Charles should appoint Sir Cornelius Vermuyden as the engineer for his undertaking bearing in mind their close association in the Hatfield venture and in spite of all the hazards through which it, and Vermuyden, had passed. Furthermore, Vermuyden was on the spot. He had an intimate knowledge of the Great Level and he had the workmen already there. In the year 1638, Vermuyden prepared for the King's information his 'Discourse Touching the Draining of the Great Fennes', subsequently published early in 1642, in which he gave a comprehensive review of the state of the Great Level, a statement of what he considered should be done there, and of how he proposed to do it. If Charles's abortive undertaking produced nothing else it must be credited with this important document in which, for the first time, we have in writing a clear statement of Vermuyden's principles of drainage.

The publication of the 'Discourse' has been held by the opponents of Vermuyden to constitute proof and an admission of the faulty nature of his original work in the Great Level, but any accusation of this nature ignores the fact that the original scheme was designed to effect by the drainage what was laid down in the Lynn Law, while the scheme propounded in the 'Discourse' was designed to produce something of much wider extent. Vermuyden quite clearly states that the Earl of Bedford 'did undertake the drayning of the said great and vast level so far as to make it summer ground' meaning that the land was to be made 'fit for meadow, or arable, or pasture' during the summer months only. It is true that there is no such definite and limited stipulation in the Lynn Law, but in the year 1630 before any comprehensive scheme of drainage had even been completed in the Great Level the generally held opinion was that the accomplishment of 'summer grounds' was all that could ever be expected. According to Vermuyden, the original adjudication of 1637 was that the land had been made 'summer ground' and that, therefore, the Earl was entitled to his recompense, but by the year 1638, when at least some form of comprehensive scheme, however imperfect, had been completed, ideas expanded and it was realised that the making of 'winter grounds', i.e., 'grounds fit for meadow, or arable, or pasture', throughout the year, was reasonably possible. There is certainly justification to assume that when he was appointed engineer to the undertaking of Charles, Vermuyden found the opportunity to revise some of his ideas not unwelcome. Doubtless in the course of six or seven years defects in his original scheme had become apparent but the main reason for the modified and extended scheme set out in the 'Discourse' was the wider conception of what could be done in the Great Level. As Vermuyden said, 'The King's contract is to make these lands winter grounds, that is, to free them from the overflowing of the rivers aforesaid, so farr as by art can be devised'. A brief examination of what the 'Discourse' contained will be made later on, but in the meantime it is important to discuss a feature connected with the St. Ives Commission which may have had some influence on the career of Vermuyden in subsequent years.

During all the disputes created by the findings of the two Commissions of Sewers of 1637 and 1638 Oliver Cromwell the future Lord Protector was intimately concerned with events, for he was essentially a product of the Fens. He was born at Huntingdon in 1599 and he came of a family which had long had territorial possessions in the Fenland dating from the acquisition, on the dissolution of the monasteries, of the rich lands of the Abbey of Ramsey and of the nunnery of Hinchinbrooke by Richard Williams (Cromwell) the future Protector's great grandfather. Oliver himself had owned and farmed land in Huntingdon until the year 1631 when, at the age of 32, he had sold this property and leased grazing lands in the neighbourhood of St. Ives. Five years later, on the death of his uncle Sir Thomas Steward, he succeeded him as farmer of the cathedral tithes at Ely where he went to live. He then became still more intimately connected with the Fens and all their problems. In the year 1627 Oliver's uncle, Sir Oliver Cromwell, the 'Golden Knight', had disposed of Hinchinbrooke to Sir Sidney Montague and retired to his Fenland estates at Ramsey in the heart of the Great Level where he died in 1655 at the ripe age of ninety-three.

It is clear, therefore, that the Cromwell family in general must have shown interest in any proposition for the drainage of the Great Level provided, of course, that that proposition had the hall mark of practicability. Clearly they would not be interested in any of the impracticable and chimerical schemes which had been proposed in the early years of the seventeenth century. Sir Oliver and other members of the family had served conscientiously on many a Commission of Sewers, and there is no indication that either they, or Oliver himself, had any basic objections to the undertaking of the Earl of Bedford under the Lynn Law. The point should be clearly understood because Cromwell has often been erroneously pictured as siding with the commoners against a scheme of drainage of any kind being imposed on the Fens and thus becoming a popular hero. That is, in fact, far from the truth. As we know, apart from any question of fulfilment of the requirements of the Lynn Law, the adjudication of St. Ives in 1637 was unpopular from many points of view. From the commoners point of view any act of enclosure, for it amounted to nothing more than that, was bound to be unpopular. Charles had recognised this and when in 1638 he declared himself as undertaker he had decreed that pending the conclusion of the operations every man should remain in possession of his customary rights. Cromwell was undoubtedly concerned about the rights of the Commoners and had been for some years. Thus on this occasion, and perhaps for the last time, he and Charles saw eye to eye. As proof of his long-standing concern in the matter can be quoted the report of some seven years earlier, not at the time of the adjudication of Huntingdon in 1638 as sometimes erroneously stated, that 'Mr. Cromwell of Ely had undertaken, they the Commoners paying him a groat for every cow they had upon the Common, to hold the drainers in suit of law for 5 years, and that in the meantime they should enjoy every part of their Common'.[1] This may have been a somewhat rash undertaking and one difficult of fulfilment, but, luckily perhaps for Cromwell, it was a piece of bluff which was never called.

[1] *Cal. State Papers Domestic, Charles I,* CCXXX. 50.

Cromwell certainly gained notoriety in the Fenland by his interest in the affairs of the Commoners, but this notoriety was somewhat local in character although it became extravagantly magnified by historians in later years. For example, it has been said that by these actions he gained the popular title of 'Lord of the Fens' but, to be quite honest, this is more or less nonsense. It was some years after the passing of the Pretended Act of 1649, with which we shall deal later, that the title of 'Lord of the Fens' was conferred on certain of the Participants in whom the control of the workings of the Company of Adventurers was vested, qualification for this title being the ownership of 500 acres of land in the Great Level. There is, indeed, nothing to show that Oliver Cromwell was ever given this title ever as a matter of courtesy.

But it will be clear from the foregoing that the Lord Protector, when he came to power, had plenty of justification for interest in the drainage of the Great Level. Possibly, and very probably, in his days at Ely and St. Ives he knew Sir Cornelius Vermuyden and it is more than probable that the latter used this acquaintanceship, it may, indeed, have been a friendship, to further his own ends after the Monarchy had disappeared. And this may be some explanation of the curiously confidential relationship which presumably existed between the two men in later years, of which, unfortunately, we have so little information. At the time of which we are speaking, however Vermuyden remained somewhat in the background in comparison to the conspicuous position which he had occupied in the Hatfield adventure. This was, perhaps, only natural since he had not been the principal undertaker for the drainage of the Great Level. That unenviable seat was occupied by Francis, Earl of Bedford. Vermuyden was only a salaried employee, at least so it appeared to the casual observer.

It is not intended now to discuss in detail Vermuyden's 'Discourse'. That will be done later when by a fuller analysis we shall attempt to show that its author was not the inept bungler, as some would have us believe, obsessed by principles of land reclamation applicable to the Netherlands, but out of place in the Fens of England. The importance of the 'Discourse' lies, in the fact that it is the only remaining written evidence which we have today of what Vermuyden's ideas of drainage were, and of the principles upon which he based his practice.

Certainly from an unbiased examination of the 'Discourse' it would be difficult to see this as other than a brilliant appreciation of the situation and a masterly exposition of the methods of draining to be adopted, irrespective of whether those methods were right or wrong. Vermuyden may have been an egotist, he may have been unscrupulous, but his 'Discourse'

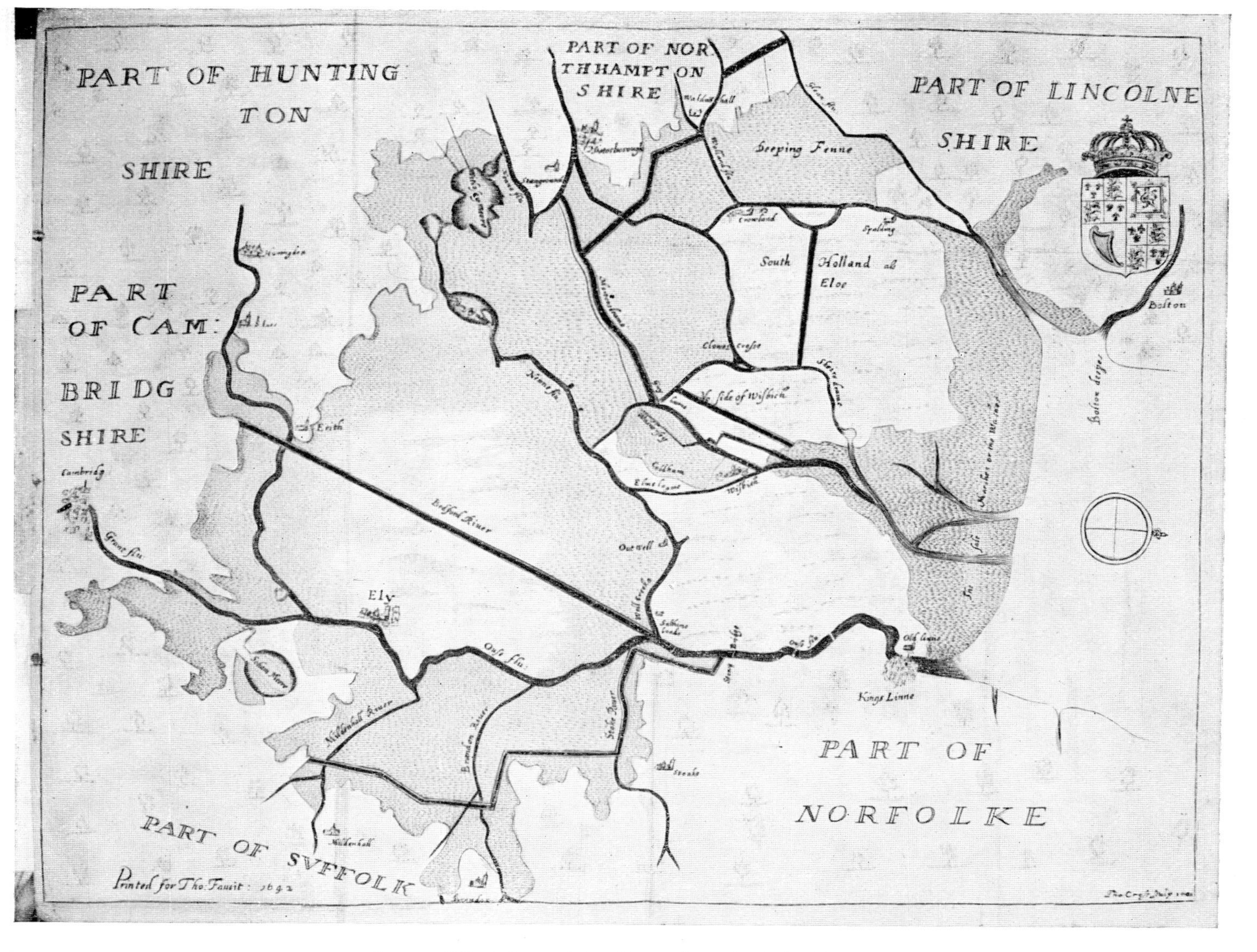

Plate IV. Map of the Great Level of the Fens.

From Vermuyden's *Discourse touching the Drayning of the Great Fennes*, London, 1642.

which must have resulted from a vast amount of work, shows that behind whatever unpleasant characteristics he may have possessed lay a very real ability and clarity of mind.

Strictly speaking the 'Discourse' was designed to apply to an area somewhat greater than that actually included in the boundaries of the Great Level, apparently because Charles on the prompting of Vermuyden had agreed to the wider application of the scheme. This was implied in the full title which read "A Discourse Touching the draining of the Great Fennes lying within the several counties of Lincoln, Northampton, Huntingdon, Norfolke, Suffolke, Cambridge and the Isle of Ely, etc.'. The title specifically does not say 'The Great Level of the Fens',—and Vermuyden was, in fact, including in the scheme land which, while certainly comprising fens, was outside the Great Level as precisely laid down in William Hayward's survey of 1635–6. For example, when defining 'The Situation of the Great Fennes' Vermuyden says that 'the level lieth in six counties . . . and bounds on the north-west on the river of Glean'. This boundary involved the inclusion of Deeping Fen in Lincolnshire, certainly excluded from Hayward's survey and also from the clear definition of the boundaries of the Great Level incorporated in the later Act of 1663 in the reign of Charles II. This expansion of the Level by Vermuyden does not materially affect any evaluation of his 'Discourse' although it does involve him in a consideration of the outfall of the river Welland (of which the Glen is a tributary) even though in point of fact the Welland did not contribute materially to the drainage of any part of the Great Level as such. Vermuyden's map, drawn by Thos. Crosse, which accompanied the 'Discourse', makes this point clear in spite of the general obscurity of the map itself and it will be apparent both from this map, and from Badeslade's, that it was the Nene and the Ouse, with all the former's many branches and the tributaries of the latter, which were vital to the Great Level. But, and this is a point of obvious importance and one emphasised earlier, the outfalls of these rivers were a long way outside the northern boundary of the Level, or as Vermuyden himself said 'The aforesaid three out-falls are of great length before they come to the sea, the lands of Holland and Marsh-land being great countries which lye between them, and do hinder the speedy current of the waters towards the sea'. This will be appreciated from an examination of Badeslade's map.

Clearly it was elementary reasoning to conclude that on the condition of the outfalls of the main rivers the drainage of the Level was wholly dependent and, therefore, it was to the condition of the outfalls that Vermuyden referred very early in his 'Discourse'. He concluded that 'Welland and Wisbech [R. Nene] out-falls are choaked every summer: but the outfall of Lynn [R. Ouse] hath sufficient water to keep open his channel'. It must not be overlooked that the main reason why the Ouse and all its tributaries had deserted the river Nene some centuries earlier was the choked condition of the outfall below Wisbech. Vermuyden went on to say that 'it is not only to be feared, but apparent, that in process of time, the out-falls of Wisbech and Welland will utterly decay . . . if they should remain as they now are'. Nor was he content to leave it at that. Later on, in detailing the work which he suggests should be done, and remember that, although a man of much influence, he was not a free agent, he could only make suggestions, he says that 'I advise to bring the aforesaid rivers Welland and Nene into one, that they may (in time) gain themselves a natural channel, which will be far better than to leave them to sundry outfalls'. Apart from any other question, it will be apparent therefore, that there was a very good reason why Vermuyden wanted to include the Welland in his scheme which would not have been possible had he confined himself to the true boundaries of the Great Level. Added to the Nene the Welland was to improve the outfall at Wisbech to the benefit of both. Vermuyden also remarked in this connection that Sir Clement Edmonds, in his report of 1618, had stated 'that upon examination it was found that anciently the waters of Welland and Neane went to the sea by Wisbech outfall'. And he also added that 'by the said report, it was likewise found good to draw the waters to their ancient outfalls, which confirms me in my resolution'. Sound reasoning, as far as it went, but not, as we shall show later, entirely convincing.

At the time when Vermuyden was writing there were two distinct schools of thought as to the methods to be employed in draining fen lands. It was recognised, of course, by both schools that the object was, in the case of heavy rainfall, to get the water away to and through the river outfalls as quickly as possible. The danger of the flooding of the low-lying grounds was not due primarily to the water or rain which fell on those grounds themselves but to the danger of the overtopping or breaching of the river banks by the water falling on and flowing down from the uplands in which they had their source. Both schools realised that the more rapid discharge of the main rivers could only be achieved if the outfalls were clear but, as far as the interior work on the rivers was concerned their ideas were widely divergent. The one school, represented by Westerdyke, was firmly of the opinion that the only course to adopt was to deepen existing rivers and embank them to confine the flow within narrow limits and so increase the velocity. Vermuyden, as we know, firstly from his work at Hatfield and secondly from the Bedford River, was convinced that the proper remedy was to replace the winding tortuous courses of the fenland rivers by new and artificial straight cuts and thus produce the increased velocity. Theoretically there is something to be said for both these systems. Practically, and from the nature of the soil available to make banks, the principle of embanking in the Fens was wrong. Vermuyden, in his arguments against embanking, said that his object was 'to avoid multiplicity of banks, which are very chargeable both in their making and maintaining'. In the 'Discourse' he was true to his principle of new straight cuts and of 'washes', employed at Hatfield and to be used, as he said, as 'receptacles for the water in time of extremity to bed on upon all occasions of floods'. And here again he was in due time to fall foul of his bitter rival Westerdyke.

So much and no more of the 'Discourse' shall we detail now. It is enough to show in broad outline the conception which Vermuyden had in mind in 1638. How much freedom had been permitted to him in the Earl of Bedford's undertaking it is difficult to say and to what extent the work which had led to the adjudications of 1637 and 1638 represented his original scheme will be discussed in a later section when examining contemporary criticisms. Whatever experience he had, or had not, had in the Netherlands, there was now behind him the experience, somewhat bitter perhaps, of Hatfield Chase, and that gained from the early work in the Great Level. Quite clearly he had applied to the Great Level much thought and observation of which the 'Discourse' was the result. There is no sign of hesitation in the expression of his views. He was convinced in his own mind how the work should be done and was not afraid to say so.

CHAPTER NINE

The Civil War. Work in Great Level suspended. Pelham's Committee orders printing of 'Discourse', 1642. Sir Philibert Vernatti arrested as a Royalist. The story of Col. Vermuyden.

IN the year 1638 when Vermuyden had presented his *Discourse Touching the Draining of the Great Level* to the King, the growing differences between Charles and the Commons had become more intelligible to the general mass of the people through the medium of the simple issue of Ship Money, to pay or not to pay. The role of martyr in the peoples' cause which had been filled somewhat flamboyantly by John Hampden had every justification for its popularity, but no legality, as was proved by the verdict of the twelve judges, seven of whom in 1641 declared absolutely for the Crown. But from that time Charles's difficulties continued to mount up, culminating at last in 1640 in the impeachment of Strafford by that arch parliamentarian John Pym, and his subsequent trial and execution in May of the following year. From that moment the breach had opened too wide ever to be healed and by August 1642, when Charles raised his standard at Nottingham Castle, there could have been no turning back on either side. Nor during the years between 1638 and 1642 could Charles give much attention to the draining of the Fens in which, there is little doubt, he had a very genuine interest not wholly conditioned by any question of financial gain.

And so circumstances had made it inevitable that by the replacement of Vermuyden's original patron, Francis Earl of Bedford, by the King whose other commitments were far too pressing and vital, the drainage scheme in the Great Level of the Fens was relegated to the back of the stage there to remain for eleven years, although not entirely forgotten. It was not until the year 1649, after Charles had died on the scaffold, that the Great Level of the Fens and its drainage were once more to play a part of importance in the affairs of a wearied and distracted country.

The Fenland counties of Cambridgeshire, Huntingdonshire, and Lincolnshire themselves played no inconspicuous part in the struggle of the

Civil War. With the rising importance of the Fen-born Oliver Cromwell and the growing influence of the Eastern Association this was bound to be the case, and while none of the decisive battles such as Marston Moor, Naseby, and others were fought on Fenland soil there is little doubt that the development of Cromwell's practical and strategic brilliance, which must be admitted whatever may be considered his other less admirable qualities, and the foundations of the New Model Army, had their origin in his early experiences with the troops of the Eastern Association.

And what can we say of Vermuyden during those fruitless eleven years when it was not even possible to maintain the completed drainage works let alone engage in fresh enterprises. Regrettably we have little on which any accurate statement can be based.

The patronage which had been extended to Vermuyden by both James and Charles, his close connection with Sir Robert Heath and others of the Court of Charles who still maintained their loyalty to the Crown must have predisposed him to the Royalist side if he had searched his soul for light on the decision without regard for material issues. But, and some might say regrettably, there is no evidence to show that his sympathies after August 1642 had any Royalist tendencies. Indeed the evidence points all the other way and if this might be construed into an abandonment of loyalties, dispassionate reflection will produce the conclusion that Vermuyden, a Dutchman in spite of his naturalisation, was not faced with the same difficult choice as faced the Englishmen of those days. Even if, as we have concluded already, Vermuyden customarily placed his own interests before all others, how can he be blamed for professing loyalty to Parliament rather than to the King if he believed, and rightly so as events were to prove, that Parliament was the only agency through which the drainage of the Great Level could be developed and by which his own interests would best be served. There is nothing to show that he took any active part in the struggle between King and Parliament and all that can be concluded is that from the year 1638, the year of the 'Discourse', to the opening of the Civil War in 1642, and during all the changing phases of that war between the year 1642 and the tragic end of Charles in January 1649, Vermuyden's chief activities were directed to an endeavour to keep intact the work already accomplished in the Great Level and to obtain legal powers to continue with the development of the drainage on the lines laid down in the 'Discourse'. The mere declaration by Charles in 1638 of himself as undertaker had resulted in little more than intention, and no decisive steps had been taken in Parliament to make that declaration legal and statutory. Indeed, on 25th January, 1641, before the final break between King and Parliament had come, the House of Commons jealous, perhaps, of any authority which Vermuyden might believe derived from the King, had resolved 'That Sir Cornelius Vermeuden [*sic*] shall be forthwith summoned to attend this House, to give an Account by what Authority he goeth on with his Works in the Fens, in the Isle of Eley; and to bring with him his Commission, or Warrant, by which he doth the same.'[1]

Clearly from this entry Vermuyden was still at that time endeavouring to forward the work and, no doubt, his summons to Parliament was the direct result of ill-favoured reports from Fenlanders holding fundamental objections to all schemes of drainage. In the end, however, these petitions and the summoning of Vermuyden resulted in the Commons taking some notice of the Great Level and passing a Resolution on 16th February, 1641, that the whole matter should be referred to a Committee under the chairmanship of Mr. Pelham. It was, in fact on 22nd February that this Committee ordered the printing of the 'Discourse'.[2] But there, for the time being, the matter ended and in the press of more urgent business nothing decisive was achieved.

While, as has been said, there is no evidence to show that Sir Cornelius played an active part on either side in the Civil War, his materialistic sympathies may have been justifiably on the side of Parliament. And this does not necessarily warrant any accusation of treachery to his adopted king, or of abandoned loyalties. Certainly Sir Philibert Vernatti, one of his original co-adventurers at Hatfield Chase, and a signatory to the Indenture of Fourteen Parts, remained staunch to his Royal Patron. On 2nd May, 1643, the Commons resolved that 'Sir Phelibert [*sic*] Vernatti be committed prisoner, to the Serjeant's Custody, for being in actual Arms against Parliament', and, rather illogically perhaps, it was ordered 'that Sir Phelibert Vernatti, and Mr. Geary do forthwith pay unto the Soldiers that brought them up, Thirty pounds for their service and Pains in bringing them up; or otherwise, that the Soldiers shall have the Cloaths, and other Goods and Things, taken upon them; and if they shall make payment of the Thirty Pounds presently, that they shall have restored unto them such Things, as have been seized or taken from them'.[3]

But if there is nothing to show for Sir Cornelius, there certainly exists documentary evidence to prove that in the Parliamentary Army there was a Colonel Vermuyden, and while it has often been assumed that this was a son of Sir Cornelius, an example of the son fighting against his father's

[1] *Journal of the House of Commons.* Vol. II., p. 394.
[2] *Journals of the House of Commons.* Vol. II., p. 434.
[3] *Journals of the House of Commons.* Vol. III., pp. 66–67.

former patron, as one writer has slightingly suggested, so far no positive proof of the assumption has yet been forthcoming. The ascertainable facts are as follows.

At the battle of Marston Moor on 2nd July, 1644, the cavalry regiments which took part in the engagement consisted of Cromwell's own regiment of fourteen troops; Manchester's regiment of horse of eleven troops, Colonel Vermuyden's five troops of horse, Colonel Fleetwood's six troops, and Manchester's regiment of dragoons consisting of five companies. In addition to being in command of a regiment of cavalry Colonel Vermuyden was quarter-master-general of Manchester's army.[1]

Marston Moor, although a bitter defeat for the Royalist forces, was not a complete disaster and it was not very long before the King and his army were again proving a very sharp thorn in the side of the Parliamentary forces. On 13th May, 1645, intelligence reached Parliament that Charles had marched to Worcester and it was concluded that his intention was to advance on Chester in the hopes of raising the siege of that city. In a letter from the Committee of both kingdoms to the Earl of Leven it was stated that 'we apprehend the danger and disorder that may ensue if he the King should march further and enter into Lancashire and Yorkshire, where in all probability the disaffection of many in those parts may furnish his army with very great numbers'. Consequently on the same day a letter was sent by the Committee to Colonel Vermuyden advising him of the situation and instructing him to march northwards 'into the parts about Leicester and Ashby-de-la-Zouch' with 2,000 horse and 500 dragoons and there to get into touch with the Earl of Leven and receive instructions to join the Scottish Army to bar the King's advance.[2]

Sir Cornelius Vermuyden had six sons in all, two of whom died in infancy, and the eldest, Cornelius, was the only one who could have been old enough to take an active part in the Civil War. It is not possible to say with certainty in what year Cornelius was born, but it might have been as early as 1625, in which case by the year 1645, when we hear so much of Colonel Vermuyden and his cavalry, Cornelius might have been twenty years of age. It would be rash to assume that this was too tender an age at which to hold a colonelcy in the Parliamentary army. Indeed there is evidence which might show that Colonel Vermuyden was young which fact appears to have annoyed Colonel Fiennes when ordered by the Committee to place himself and his troops under the command of Vermuyden. Fiennes objected and on 19th May, 1645 the Committee were writing to him saying that 'when we

[1] C. H. Firth, *Marston Moor*, Trans. R. Hist. Soc. Vol. XII, 1898.

[2] *Cal. State Paper Dom. Charles I*, 1645. Vol. DVII, pp. 485–486.

appointed the party going to the assistance of the Scots' army to be placed under the command of Col. Vermuyden, we conseived that he was the eldest of the colonels, but we have since been otherwise informed.' At the same time they wrote to Vermuyden giving him more intelligence of the situation and telling him that 'when we appointed this party . . . we did not know there were any elder colonels appointed to go with you' and enjoining him to deal with the situation with the tact which it clearly required.[1]

On these grounds, therefore, it might be assumed that Colonel Vermuyden was young in years, and young enough to be the son of Cornelius Vermuyden, but there is also the possibility that the Committee, in using the phrases 'the eldest of the colonels' and 'any elder colonels' were referring not to age but to seniority, although the two might go hand in hand.

In the so-called *Squires Papers*, accepted by Thomas Carlyle as genuine, there appeared a letter reputedly written 18th July, 1643 by Henry Cromwell, son of Oliver Cromwell, to 'Captain Berry at his Quarters, Whittlesea', in which he says that 'Vermuyden has sent his son on to say we had better push on three troops as scouts, as far as Stamford, and hold Peterborough at all costs'. It has been pointed out that 'this letter with its rather stilted language, from a beardless youth of fifteen, tells rather against the authenticity',[2] and this opinion has been borne out by later judgement which has pronounced the *Squires Papers* as forgeries concocted after the first publication of Carlyle's *Letters and speeches of Oliver Cromwell* and palmed off on Carlyle by William Squire. Carlyle accepted the authenticity of the transcripts sent to him by Squire without ever seeing the originals which, in fact, never existed, and published them in December 1847.[3]

If the detractors of Sir Cornelius Vermuyden such as Samuel Wells had wished to discredit him further, and had they known the facts, they might have fastened on to the true story that Col. Vermuyden was arrested in 1645, and have ignored the fact that on 28th June, 1645, he was brought before the Bar of the House of Lords by a Habeas Corpus, and released on the information that, 'the State owes Colonel Vermuyden more money than Five Hundred Pounds, which is the sum he is arrested for'.[4] This seems to have determined the Colonel that England was no place for him and on 4th July ten days before the battle of Naseby he was granted a pass 'to go out of England'.[5]

[1] *Cal. State Paper Dom. Charles I.* 1645. Vol. DVII, p. 504.
[2] A. Kingston. *East Anglia and the Great Civil War.* 1897, p. 117.
[3] C. H. Firth Intro. to S. C. Lomas ed. *Letters and speeches of Oliver Cromwell*, 1904.
[4] *Journals. House of Lords.*
[5] Proc. Committee of Both Kingdoms. *Cal. State Paper Dom. Charles I.* Vol. DX.

Who was Colonel Vermuyden? The related facts prove nothing. He may have been Cornelius the son of Sir Cornelius and if that was the case then he must have returned to England before January 1646, because on the 19th of that month it was recorded in the Proceedings of the Committee of the Fens that 'Two papers were delivered in unto the Committee. The one under the hand of Sir Cornelius Vermuyden. The other under the hand of Cornelius Vermuyden, Esq. his sonne both purporting their reasons for the feasibility of that worke of draining the Great Level'.[1] Now, if Cornelius the son was old enough in 1646 to submit a report of this nature to the Committee, presumably he would have been old enough in 1645 to be a colonel in the Parliamentary army, even if he was not 'the eldest of the Colonels'. But against this, there is in existence a document which tends to show that the Colonel Vermuyden had the initial 'B', but so far it has not been possible to find a Vermuyden to fit the initial. And so the story remains one of uncertainty and while it is of comparative unimportance, it does provide an interesting sidelight on the Vermuyden story during the comparatively barren period of the Civil War, barren, that is, from the point of view of the work of drainage of the Great Level. Furthermore, if Colonel Vermuyden was the son of Sir Cornelius, his service in the Parliamentary cavalry may have had its origin in the father's friendship with Oliver Cromwell, which, as later events tend to show, must have existed.

Francis, Earl of Bedford, to whom so much of the credit for the initial undertaking in the Great Level is due, whatever may have been his motives, never lived to see the opening of the Civil War. A few days after the execution of Strafford he died of smallpox on 9th May, 1641. The adventure of the Great Level had strained considerably the fortunes of the Russell family and William, who succeeded his father as fifth earl, found himself faced with very difficult circumstances, both personal and national. His protean vacillations between the Royalists and the Parliamentarians are a matter of general history, but it is impossible to forbear from wondering how much his final choice of the Parliamentary side was influenced by the realisation that it was the one side from which he had any hope of further participation in the work of draining in the Great Level, and thus of retrieving some, at least, of the family fortunes.

Regrettably there is nothing in the archives at Woburn which would throw any light either on the motives of William or on any of the negotiations and discussions which must have taken place between his father and Cornelius Vermuyden at the time of, and subsequent to, the Lynn Law and Indenture of Fourteen parts. As Miss Gladys Scott Thomson has informed

[1] Fen Office Documents.

the present writer 'Except for a few isolated letters and his portentous theological musings nothing has survived of the 4th Earl of Bedford, no accounts, no political papers, nothing or next to nothing for the estate. The destruction in view of his political position may have been deliberate. The papers of his son, the 5th Earl, only begin to be extensive after 1660. There again there is nothing for the Fens'.

Fortunately, not long after the beginning of the Civil War, there are other sources of materials which provide some insight into the matters of the Great Level, and of Sir Cornelius Vermuyden himself, soon to enter on a further stage of his career, the stage which was to prove the last in his story of the Great Level.

CHAPTER TEN

Death of Charles I. Andrewes Burrell's pamphlets. Passing of Pretended Act, 1649. Proceedings of the Adventurers and discussions on appointment of Vermuyden as Director of Works.

EVEN if, as we know, the work of the drainage of the Great Level was of necessity in a state of abeyance during the varying phases of the Civil War from 1642 up to the execution of Charles in January 1649, nevertheless it was a subject to which Parliament, in spite of all its other pre-occupations, continued during that period to give considerable, if at times somewhat perfunctory, attention. The main significance of this fact is that quite clearly Parliament appreciated the value of the Great Level and although, perhaps, in the early stages of this period Oliver Cromwell had not the power or influence which he possessed later, yet it can reasonably be concluded that his influence, founded, perhaps, on his friendship with Sir Cornelius Vermuyden, was not negligible in the passing of the so-called Pretended Act in May 1649. But that, perhaps, is to anticipate somewhat.

When Charles had engaged Vermuyden in 1638, and when in that year Vermuyden had prepared his 'Discourse', the hope and intention had been that ultimately the scheme laid down therein should be put into execution forthwith, but, in actual fact, neither time nor money was available for this ambitious plan, and in the end all that Vermuyden was able to carry out for his royal patron and employer before August 1642 was the minor work of building a bank on the south side of Morton's Leam, a new cut 60 feet wide and 2 miles long in the river Nene to improve the outfall below Wisbech, a sluice at Stanground to turn the waters of the Nene into Morton's Leam, and a sluice at the outfall of Shire Drain.[1] These were merely works of improvement and involved no new principle of drainage.

In the year 1641 and before the publication of Vermuyden's 'Discourse' Andrewes Burrell published his pamphlet entitled 'An Explanation of

[1] W. DUGDALE, *op. cit.*, p. 414.

Drayning Workes which have been lately made for the Kings Majestie in Cambridgeshire, By the Direction of Sir Cornelius Vermuyden . . . Wherein is discovered how the said Sir Cornelius hath abused the King's Majestie, and many of his loving subjects'. Andrewes Burrell owned lands in the neighbourhood of Waldersey on the banks of the Nene above Wisbech and he was, therefore, interested in the drainage works as affecting that area.

His criticisms of Vermuyden are given under six headings. The first part of his indictment concerns methods of construction. He accuses him of making 'hollow and counterfeit Bankes of light Moore, Hassocks, and Sedge' and goes on to say that 'he hath disgraced the King's works in causing divers Sluices and Sasses to be made of rotten timber.' Then he continues:

'Fourthly, he hath abused the King in misspending his treasure.' 'Fifthly, he hath abused the late Earle of Bedford and divers Noblemen and Gentlemen that adventured with him in his undertaking by undervaluing the Workes which they made, and by hindering their proceedings . . .'

'Sixthly, he hath abused divers of his Majesties subjects, in taking their lands from them illegally, without any composition or satisfaction.'

The accusation concerning the 'bankes of light Moore' may have had some justification. In many places only peat soil was available for the construction of banks, a fact of which Vermuyden was fully aware and which he adduced as one of his arguments in the 'Discourse' in favour of his plan by which the use of banks could be reduced to a minimum. As for the 'misspending' of the Kings treasure, this is an accusation which could easily be made without substantiation. What would appear to be Burrell's trouble was that he was suffering under a grievance, partly due, as he felt, to the fact that certain of his land in Waldersey had been taken, under unsatisfactory terms of compensation, to form part of one of Vermuyden's 'washes' there. We know, however, that in 1650 and 1651 Burrell still owned nearly four hundred acres of land in Waldersey Wash part of which he leased and part sold to William, Earl of Bedford, and, what is more, in 1642, the year after the publication of his pamphlet, he was still purchasing lands in Waldersey from John Rous of Henham, Suffolk.[1] He had, incidentally, been one of the original signatories to the Indenture of Fourteen Parts. Proof of his sense of grievance of another kind lies in his own words when he tells us that Vermuyden used his lands 'of a purpose to doe me a mischiefe, in regard I did contravert some of his opinions before the late Lord Treasurer, when myselfe was a Commissioner for His Majesty in October 1638.' It is not to be supposed that Vermuyden designed Waldersey Wash on purpose to annoy

[1] Middle Level Commissioners' Documents.

Andrewes Burrell, but perhaps the annoyance was largely caused by that lack of tact and by the blunt imperiousness of which we have had evidence earlier.

Concerning the work of draining which was done by Francis Earl of Bedford, Burrell tells us that 'I have often heard Sir Cornelius slight all the workes which were made by the late Earl, as if they were rather hurtful than beneficial to the country' and later goes on to remark that 'the Earle opened Wysbeach River to the Sea, and kept the sea from choking it again . . . a worke farre exceeding all that Sir Cornelius hath done' but from the evidence at our disposal it would appear that Vermuyden himself carried out this work after the King had become the sole Adventurer. As to Burrell's suggestion that Vermuyden's 'plot is by subtilty to rob the late Earle and those Adventurers of the credit of their works', it might be that Vermuyden was endeavouring to curry favour with Charles by disparaging the work which had been done by the original Adventurers. But if this is true then the only conclusion which we can reach is that that work was not what Vermuyden himself had desired as otherwise he would have been disparaging his own work. What does appear from this is that Vermuyden had not been given a free hand by the Adventurers and this throws some considerable light on his later conduct towards, and his dealings with, William, fifth Earl of Bedford and his co-Adventurers after the passing of the Pretended Act in 1649. The pity is that we have no copy of Vermuyden's original map and scheme of the year 1630 or so.

Andrewes Burrell's outpourings had little, if any, effect at the time on Vermuyden, or on the course of the drainage of the Great Level, but in helping us now to interpret one phase of Vermuyden's career they achieve a result which Burrell never foresaw nor hoped for. Apart from this, the naively enlightening final paragraph of his pamphlet unwittingly exposes a further grievance.

'Lastly, if it be objected, that I have informed against Sir Cornelius in discontent, or because he by his subtilty did defeat me of my imployment in those Workes . . . and cannot justifie every particular which is here expressed; . . . let me undergoe the displeasure of all them whose help I doe emplore.'

In 1642 after the publication of Vermuyden's 'Discourse', Burrell returned to the attack with another pamphlet entitled 'Exceptions against Sir Cornelius Virmudens Discourse for the Draining of the great Fennes etc . . . Wherein His Majesty was mis-informed and abused, in regard it wanteth all the essentiall parts of a Designe . . .' But by the year 1646 he appears to have changed his outlook, for on 25th February of that year he gave evidence before the Committee of the House of Commons and was reported as follows.

'Andrewes Burrell of Wisbech, gent. sayeth that hee conceives it [the drainage] very feasible and sayeth that after the Earl of Bedford had made his workes which were not finished the mane body of the Fennes were not drowned in summer time for 7 years together. That in 1632 or 33 when the head of Bedford River was set out the mane body of the Fennes were drowned that yeare on the 14th August and after the making of that River the mane body of the fennes were usually drie about the beginning of May for 7 yeares together with one yeare the first April. That it will be very profitable to the Common Wealth for lands of his owne in Wisbech and Elme that was not worth any thing before the workes were made and after the makings of the workes have been worth to him 300^{li} yeare by sowing of cole seed upon the lande.'[1]

From this it does not appear that Andrewes Burrell had many grounds for complaint against the effectiveness of the works which Vermuyden had carried out in the first undertaking, and while the pamphlets which he published in 1641 and 1642 have little intrinsic value, representing, as they do, the airing of imaginary grievances of a disappointed man who had been 'defeated' of his employment in the works of drainage, yet they have a certain importance which merits their consideration. First of all it should be said that Andrewes Burrell was one of the family of William Burrell who, it will be recalled, was alleged by Sir Anthony Thomas to have conspired with Sir Thomas Crooke in 1629 in an endeavour to obtain by illegal, or underhand, means the contract for the draining of the Great Level. But the main distinction which Andrewes Burrell's pamphlet have is that they were the first of a long line of similar publications critical of Vermuyden, and, from the historians point of view, the difficulty has been that the criticisms which the pamphlets, and many others continuing down to the nineteenth century, expressed have too often been accepted without any question. Thus, while Burrell's pamphlets have been quoted and their findings held against Vermuyden, his later testimony of 1646, which to all intents and purposes refutes everything which he said in earlier years, has remained unknown,and certainly unquoted. This has been in general the manner in which most appraisals of Vermuyden's work and conduct have been made.

The Committee before which Burrell gave his evidence had been appointed under the chairmanship of Pelham in January 1641, some seven months before the beginning of the Civil War, to examine the question of the drainage of the Great Level. During the early phases of the struggle the

[1] Fen Office Documents.

Committee did little effective, as was to be expected, but on 16th May, 1646, its deliberations began to have an air of purpose. This was undoubtedly a reflection from the wider world of the Great Rebellion as it was in the early days of May of that year that Charles had surrendered to the Scots at Southwell and the hope had been born, still-born as events were to prove, that perhaps peace and a democratic combination of Monarchy and Parliament might be achieved. In the meantime, however, Parliament had been far from idle, for as the minutes of the Committee for 16th May, 1646, show, they had drawn up an Ordinance for draining the Great Level and on that day the Committee resolved that a letter should be written to the Sheriffs of all the counties concerned 'to give notice to the inhabitants that an Ordinance is referred to the Committee . . . and that such as desire to be heard should attend this Committee the first Thursday in June next'.[1] The next step a few days later was the calling of William, Earl of Bedford, before a sub-Committee appointed to examine the interest and title that he had in the draining, and the money which had been expended in his father's original adventure. It was on 1st June, 1646, that 'Mr. Thorpe reported from the sub-Committee . . . that the Earle of Bedford came into the same business upon the Petition of the Country', and the Lynn Law of 1630 was quoted to show the terms upon which the undertaking had been based. What, in effect, the primary conclusions of the Committee amounted to was an affirmation of the right of William, Earl of Bedford, as 'son and heir of the said Francis, late Earl of Bedford', still to be considered the undertaker for the drainage of the Great Level in spite of the adjudications of St. Ives and Huntingdon in 1637 and 1638, and in spite, also of the subsequent declaration of Charles of his assumption of the undertaking. Having reached this conclusion which was somewhat revolutionary in character, then a secondary consideration on which they had to deliberate was 'Whether the works of drayninge the Great Level be favourable or not, secondly if favourable whether beneficial to the Commonwealth'. That the intended resumption of the drainage scheme was far from universally popular was clear from the fact that during June and the first part of July 1646 there are recorded in the minutes of seven meetings of the Committee no fewer than 48 petitions from the inhabitants of various parts of the Level protesting against the drainage. There was little hope that such petitions, would prevail when, as was clear, so much benefit 'to the Commonwealth' could be gained by the conversion of some 300,000 acres into profitable agricultural land, but the Committee was in no hurry to come to a final decision, and another three years were to pass before, on 29th May, 1649, 'An Act for the Draining of the Great Level

[1] *Bedford Level Proceedings*, Vo. I.

of the Fens' the so-called Pretended Act, passed the Commons. And on the same day the following entry, the first, appeared in the Proceedings of the Company of Adventurers for the draining of the Great Level.

'The Acte for drayninge the great Levell of the Fennes passed the House between the houres of 10 & 12 in the morninge. Twas desired by the Adventurers & participants that the Earles of Arundell & Bedford be desired to attend Leiu[tt] [*sic*] Gen[ll] Cromwell & Commissary Ireton to morrow morninge at 7 o clocke to return a thankful acknowledgement'.

What was this Act which had so laboriously come into being? It was, of course, a statutory recognition of William, fifth Earl of Bedford as the lawful heir to the undertaking of his father, Francis, whose works in the Great Level had, as the Act rather diffidently states, 'by reasons of some late interruptions . . . fallen into decay'. The King had been done to death and the Act makes no reference to his undertaking of 1638 except to declare null and void the Decree of Sewers at Huntingdon in that year. It was 'enacted and ordained . . . that the said William, Earl of Bedford, the said participants and adventurers, and his and their heirs and assigns, be and are hereby declared to be the undertakers of the said work of draining of the said Great Level' and restored to them was the recompense of 95,000 acres for the work of draining.

It was a simple and straightforward Act which, while it did lay down the boundaries of the Level, made no stipulation as to how the work of draining was to be carried out, as it obviously could not, except to the extent of stipulating firstly, that the work was to be finished by 10th October, 1656, and, secondly, 'that the said Earl of Bedford, participants, adventurers nor commissioners, nor any of them, shall, by any authority hereby given or granted, intermeddle with the River of Welland'. This latter point is emphasised here because, from what has been related earlier, it is clear that Vermuyden considered, and, it is hoped to show later, quite rightly considered, that the state of the River Welland and of its outfall was an important contributory factor in the draining of the Great Level. It will be recalled that he had, in effect, said so in his 'Discourse' but, unfortunately, there does not seem to be any evidence that either the Committee of the House of Commons or the Company of Adventurers constituted under the Act were prepared to admit of the existence of the 'Discourse' and the scheme of drainage which it embodied. It may be that the 'Discourse' was anathema to the Parliamentarians and their adherents owing to its Royal connection and for this reason was to them entirely non-existent. A curious perverse attitude, if this explanation is correct, but one quite understandable in the phase of bigotry and sophism then prevailing.

On 29th May, 1649, and with this first entry of the Proceedings of the

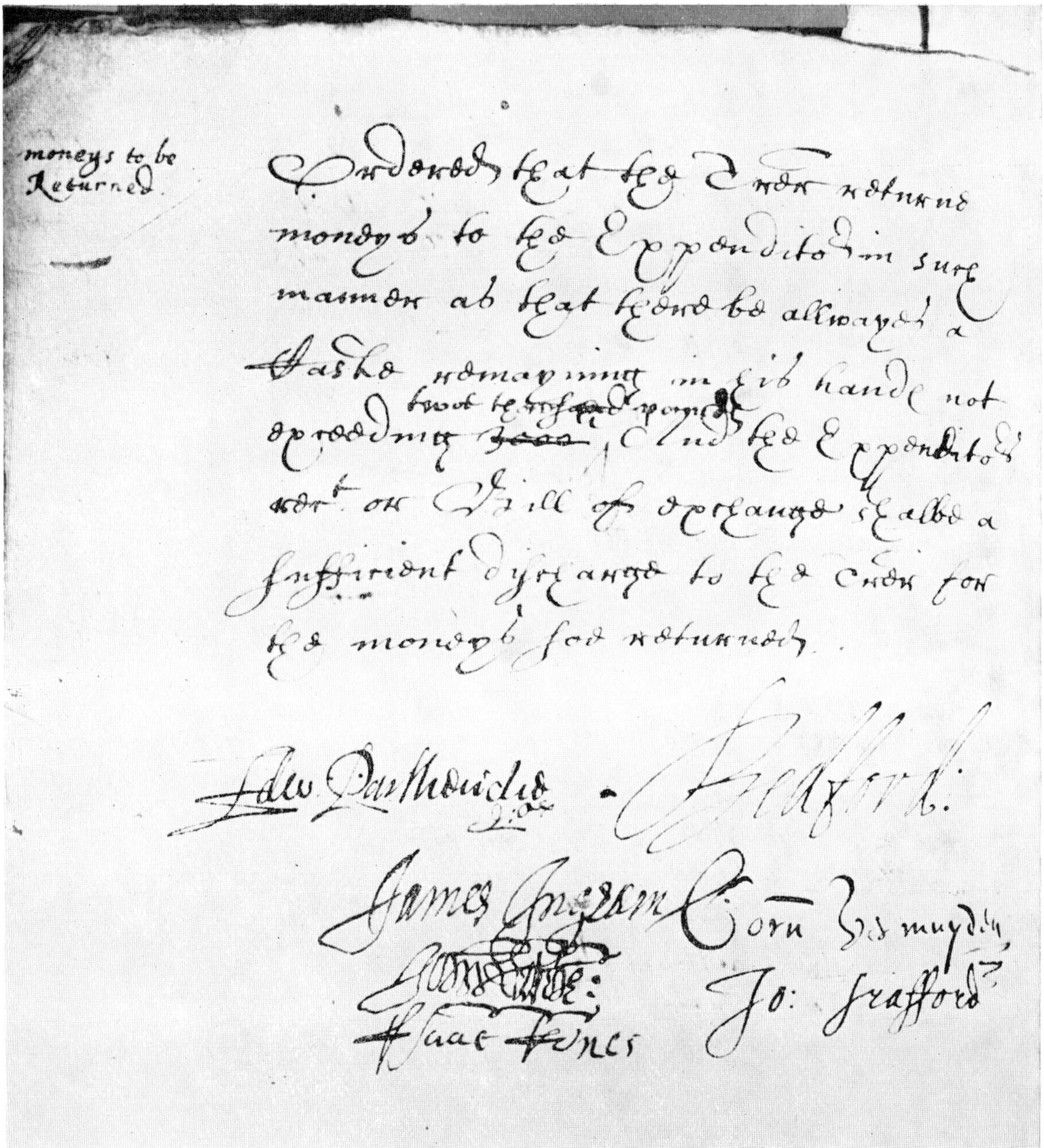

moneys to be Returned

Ordered that the Trer returne moneys to the Expenditor in such manner as that there be alwayes a stocke remayning in his hands not exceeding twoo thousand pounds, And the Expenditors wrt or Bill of exchange shalbe a sufficient discharge to the Trer for the moneys soe returned.

Edw. Partheriche

Bedford.

James Ingram

Corn. Vermuyden

James Latch:

Isaac Jones

Jo: Trafford

PLATE V. Page from the Proceedings of the Bedford Level Adventurers for the meeting held on 8 March, 1649/50.

Showing signatures of Sir Edward Partheriche (Partridge); William 5th Earl of Bedford; James Ingram; Sir Cornelius Vermuyden; James Latch; Isaac Jones and Thos. Trafford.

Adventurers begins the well documented history of the early phases of the drainage of the Great Level and there are, among others, six precious volumes of these Proceedings, now in the possession of the Great Ouse River Board, the heirs to the Bedford Level Corporation, covering the period up to 5th April 1656. That these volumes remained to the great benefit of posterity after the Great Fire of London of 1666, when the Fen Office in Mr. Hampson's chambers in the Temple, and nearly all the records of the early drainage of the Great Level, were destroyed, is due, presumably, to the fact that five of these six volumes are contemporary fair copies of the minutes written at the time of the meetings. These copies were, perhaps, made to be kept as duplicates at Ely, and were among the documents removed from the Temple to Ely by Lord Gorges shortly before the calamity. But the remaining volume contains the original minutes from which the duplicate covered by Volume III was prepared, and as such the entries are signed by one or more of the Adventurers present. Thus we have the signatures of William, Earl of Bedford, Sir Cornelius Vermuyden, Chief Justice St. John, Col. Dodson, and of many others of less importance. Furthermore, this volume contains the rough notes of the meetings of Pelham's Committee of the House of Commons. It can be conjectured that this volume was taken to Ely by mistake, but what is certain is that all these six volumes intimately concern Sir Cornelius Vermuyden up to the time of his disappearance from these records after April 1655.

It was Robert Bowyer, Clerk of the Parliaments from 1610 to 1620 who, in writing of his duties, said that 'howbeit into the journal book which is the record, he [the clerk] doth in discretion forbear to enter many things spoken, though memorable, yet not necessary nor fit to be registered and left to posterity of record.'[1] What was true of the Parliamentary journals was equally true of the Proceedings, and to get a true picture of the meetings which they record it is necessary to give the imagination some little play beyond the bare words in order to conjure up the bitter, tumultuous, and often acrimonious, clash of personalities which they sometimes baldly represent. In relation to Vermuyden, his virtues and defects, it is clearly a matter of individual interpretation of the records, but an interpretation based on a reasonable evaluation of the evidence and not on a preconceived sympathy or antipathy. Samuel Wells, appointed Register of the Bedford Level Corporation in 1824, had, of course, free access to these six volumes of Proceedings and made full use of them in his *History of the Bedford Level*, a most valuable book to all historians of the Fen drainage. But unfortunately, he had a violent antagonism against Vermuyden based, presumably, on an

[1] K. Mackenzie, *The English Parliament.* Penguin Books, London, 1950.

uncritical acceptance of the abusive and ill-founded opinions which had found their way into the many pamphlets published in the seventeenth and eighteenth centuries. These, as we have already shown, began with Andrewes Burrell's unpleasant pamphlets and continued, as we shall later show, right up to the latter part of the nineteenth century. There need be no illusions as to Vermuyden's personal peculiarities. Probably he was not a likeable character, but this is no justification for the continuing adverse criticism of the practical value of his works, even if it may be an explanation. The indictments of one writer were slavishly copied by the next without a full examination, or even a full understanding, of the facts until by 1830 Wells, without having produced any arguments, blandly and vindictively states that 'Sir Cornelius was an incubus, a night-mare which, it will be hereafter seen, the Company vainly endeavoured to shake off.' A prejudgement based on a faulty interpretation of facts. In actuality the case was very different, as we shall hope to show.

The second meeting of the Adventurers took place at 'Lord Whitelocke's house near Temple Barre' on 30th May when, headed by the Earl of Bedford, there were nine Adventurers present. The early rising necessitated by the 7 o'clock call on Cromwell had, apparently, been too much for the Earl of Arundel as he failed to put in an appearance at the meeting. Little business was done that day except that it was 'Agreed to pay and did then contribute 40^{s} apiece for discharge of the Clarkes fees of the parliament for passing and engrossing the Acte' and it was agreed that meetings should be held every Monday, Wednesday, and Friday. At the meeting on 4th June rules were drawn up for the appointment of a treasurer and a clerk and on the following day, when fourteen Adventurers were present, including the Earls of Arundel and Bedford the all important question of the appointment of a Director of the Works and of his duties was discussed. There was apparently, agreement on the general duties of the Director who, it was firstly stated, should 'appoint how and where and in what manner and when from tyme to tyme the workes or Bankes, sluices, Sasses, Rivers & Draynes are to be made & of what dimensions or length height depth breadth & the like'. Later it was laid down that 'the Director shall in all things observe the Acts of Parliament and cause the great level of the Fennes to be drayned according to the Acts'. Well, that was all straightforward and nobody could object to these motions.

Quite clearly the obvious choice for the Director was Sir Cornelius Vermuyden. He had been employed on the original undertaking, he had the additional experience of Hatfield Chase behind him and what is more he had a definite plan for the drainage. It was not surprising, therefore, that at this meeting he was 'named for the Director', but it is further minuted that, on this being done, 'debate was had whether he should not pursue and submit to such direction and order therein as he shall from tyme to tyme receive from the Adventurers or participants or the major part of them at a general meeting'. Vermuyden's name is not recorded as being present at this meeting, and he may have said little when the proposition was put to him, but that he 'desired tyme to consider of it by to morrow 3 o clock, in the Afternoon and then to deliver in his Reasons & demandes'.

Now, what were Vermuyden's reactions to the proposals, tentative though they appeared to be, for the consideration of which he required a little time? To repeat once more, he had a plan for the draining of the Great Level, a plan which had been given the fullest publicity by the appearance of the 'Discourse' in 1642 and which, therefore, had become, or could have become, common knowledge to the Adventurers in the seven years which had passed. But, according to the record of the meeting of 5th June, nobody appears to have mentioned the plan or have taken it into any account, a fact which will become more apparent later on. This in itself may have caused some surprise on Vermuyden's part, but what must have created resentment was the proposal that he should, if appointed Director, 'submit to such direction and order' as the Adventurers might think fit. On the face of it this stipulation does not appear unjustified. If Vermuyden was to be an employee of the Adventurers then logically the Adventurers should have some control over him. The matter, however, was not quite as simple as that.

There is little doubt that in the original 'adventure' Vermuyden had suffered from interference and restriction from Francis, Earl of Bedford and his fellow Adventurers and had been prevented from carrying out his plan of draining as originally intended. It is true that there is no direct documentary proof of this contention but the analysis of Andrewes Burrell's pamphlet alone leads inevitably to this conclusion. The draining of the Great Level could not be accomplished by a haphazard digging of ditches. Vermuyden knew this. He knew from experience that a comprehensively designed scheme alone could succeed. And he knew by now the type of individual in the shape of the Adventurers with whom he had to deal. Honest men, no doubt, but amateur drainers without an appreciation of the limits of their knowledge. He was aware that the possession of an earldom or a knighthood did not necessarily imply skill in drainage works. And that was why he desired time to consider, not his reply to their offer, because he knew that in its suggested form that was unacceptable, but the manner in which his reply was to be presented.

CHAPTER ELEVEN

Discussions continued, Westerdyke consulted, Col. Dodson's proposals. Failure to reach agreement. Adverse influence of Sir Edward Partridge.

THE following day the meeting was attended by only eleven Adventurers with Sir Miles Sandys at their head, both the Earls being absent. 'Sir Cornelius Vermuyden's letter was read, but nothing was done thereon. Twas desired Sir Cornelius should appear in person himself to morrow three o clocke in the Afternoone and then to deliver in his demandes and Report to the Adventurers'.

It is quite clear that at this meeting, only the fifth since the passing of the Act, the Adventurers began to realise that they were confronted with a crisis, a crisis of considerable importance to them and one created by a powerful and unyielding personality. Behind the bare record that 'Sir Cornelius Vermuyden's letter was read', and that letter must have contained the terms on which he was prepared to become Director, lies the picture of a little conclave of Adventurers, perhaps somewhat awed by Vermuyden's stand, deciding that the safest thing to do would be nothing. Except one thing. As the importance of the occasion dawned on them they 'resolved to meete every daie at 3 o clocke in the Afternoon'. The fate of the undertaking lay in the balance.

The first business to which the meeting gave its attention on the next day was this question of whether they should insist upon retaining control over the Director of Works and finally it was 'agreed to have the power of comptrollment from tyme to tyme over the Director' and that such 'comptrollment' should be exercised only on the orders of eleven Adventurers or participants of which number three at least of the following should be present, the Earl of Arundel, the Earl of Bedford, Lord Chief Justice St. John, Robert Henley and Robert Castell.

The subsequent course of events is best illustrated by the following extracts from the Proceedings:

Friday 8th June.

Insisted upon 2 points or questions to be propounded to Sir Cornelius Vermuyden.
That if Sir Cornelius Vermuyden will discover his Designe to 3 such persons as the Adventurers or the Majority part of them shall appoint, they to see his platt or Designe and assure & promise their faith not to discover to any if they not approve of it. And in case they doe approve of it, to contract with him.

2. What recompense or compensation he shall have for perfectinge the workes.
To the first agreed.
To the 2nd as touching the Recompense. Decided 7 of the Adventurers consenting to give Sir Cornelius 4000 acres, another seven agreed to give him but 2000 acres My Lord Bedford only dissenting vizt. his lordships vote was for 3000 acres but yet afterwards to turn the scale he consented to 4000 acres.

Saturday 9th June.

Sir Cornelius Vermuyden being present after much debate he promised to show his designe on Monday next to such 5 of the Adventurers as the Major part shall appoint.

Monday 11th June.

The Earle of Bedford acquainted the Adventurers with a discourse he had with a dutchman touchinge some reasons he alledged for the better performinge the worke of drayninge.

From this last entry it is quite clear the Adventurers were beginning to realise that if they were to bargain with Vermuyden they would have to have something to bargain with, and that that something would have to be an alternative plan and Director of the Works of draining. The Dutchman with whom the Earl of Bedford had had discourse was Westerdyke, a strong critic of Vermuyden, as we know, and one whose very principles of drainage were opposed to Vermuyden's. The Adventurers cannot truly be blamed for this course of action. They had a lot of money at stake and the success of the undertaking depended entirely upon the success, or failure, of the scheme of drainage adopted. It is difficult to believe that they were not acquainted with Vermuyden's scheme as laid down in the 'Discourse' although this seems to be implied in their desire that he should 'discover his Designe', unless this merely meant that they wished him to explain the scheme beyond the bare published account.

Nor can Vermuyden be criticised for the stand which he took. He may have thought, as Wells malignantly suggests, that he had the Adventurers in the hollow of his hand, but it is quite clear that he did not hold all the trump cards and a man less sure or sincere in his technical beliefs might under these circumstances have weakened and modified his demands. On the 13th June the Adventurers made it quite clear that they were prepared to receive proposals from anybody 'that will speak towards the Advancement of the drayninge (in the presence of Sir Cornelius Vermuyden)'. The following day, at the meeting attended by no fewer than nineteen Adventurers, of whom Vermuyden was now one, they considered the three petitions from the Isle of Ely praying for the appointment of Lieut. Col. Dodson as Director of the Workes and agreed that Dodson should be heard that afternoon at 4 o'clock. The meeting in the afternoon took place at Mr. Henley's house in Temple Bar, Vermuyden does not appear to have been present and

'Leiu^{tt} Colln^{el} [*sic*] Dodson declared his Designe for the setting of a Sluce [*sic*] on the River Ouse and affectinge the works of drayninge by new Rivers & not by Bankes And it was agreed that his Designe be taken into further consideration.'

Now that is a very significant entry, and the significance is twofold. Firstly it shows that Dodson accepted Vermuyden's principle of new straight drains as opposed to Westerdyke's principle of embanking existing rivers, and secondly, the expressed intention of building a Sluice on the River Ouse places some, at least, of the responsibility for Denver Sluice, so adversely criticised in later years, upon Dodson's shoulders. There will be much to be said about Denver Sluice later on. Dodson, as he was to reveal in his own words in 1664,[1] had been employed on the original undertaking of 1630, and during the Civil War appears to have had a varied career in the Parliamentary Forces finishing up as Governor of Crowland. Apart, therefore, from his martial activities, he possessed some knowledge of draining work in the Fens and was not, like so many others at the time, talking entirely without experience.

In the meantime the Adventurers rather shirked the unpleasant necessity of doing anything about Vermuyden's demands until on Saturday, 16th June they 'Resolved that Sir Cornelius Vermuyden's Demandes be taken into consideration on Monday next'. And so they were. A copy of the reply to the demands was given to Vermuyden and he was asked to give *his* final reply on the next day, Tuesday, 19th June. The entry in the Proceedings for that day gives a clear and succinct account of what happened.

'Sir Cornelius Vermuyden came & delivered in to the Adventurers his ultimate Answer in writing by way of Replication to the Adventurers Answer to his demandes formerly given and which were read over to the Adventurers And thereupon they resolved to lay it by and enter upon some other business for the present And they agreed to propound to the Lordes [Arundel, Bedford and St. John] what theire sense is thereupon And further that they thought it not fitt to depend upon Sir Cornelius Vermuyden any longer but make choice of some other to goe on with this summers worke

[1] *The Design, for the perfect draining of the Great Level of the Fens, called Bedford Level . . . by Collonel William Dodson.* Reprinted in Wells's *History of the Bedford Level*, Vol. II.

beginning on the north side of Bedford River But yet the Adventurers did then expresse that they would determyne nothing there in themselves until they received the Lordes concurrence thereon And ordered that Sir Edward Partridge and Mr. Fountayne tomorrow morning attend the Lordes for their direction therein'.

And later in the minutes of this meeting are given Sir Cornelius Vermuyden's demands, the reply to these of the Adventurers, and the final reply of Sir Cornelius on which the negotiations broke down.

What exactly were their differences and where were their demands irreconcilable? There is nothing whatever to show that any question of the method of draining the Great Level was in dispute. The Adventurers seem to have been prepared to accept Vermuyden's scheme which, apparently, he had shown to them on Monday, 11th June and which, although based on the 'Discourse' of 1642 may have been somewhat modified. To all intents and purposes the two parties had been able to reach agreement, more or less, on the terms of the recompense which was to be given to Vermuyden as, apart from the granting of the 4,000 acres, his original demand for the payment of £1,000 had been altered by him to the payment of £300 down and the balance at the rate of £30 a month in reply to the Adventurers' offer of £300 and £20 per month. This was merely pointless hair-splitting and what really angered Vermuyden was the proposed 'comptrollment' of his work by 'eleven of the Adventurers & Participants at least whom the Earl of Arundel, Earl of Bedford, Lord Chief Justice St. John, Mr. Henley and Mr. Castell or three or more of them to be of the number'. As Vermuyden knew quite clearly from past experience this did not mean that the committee were to exercise only a general control over the works of drainage, as they were justifiably entitled to do, but that they would have and exercise the right to decide how much of his scheme was to be carried out. As he himself, said, the effect would be that he would be subjected to cries of 'expend not so much, do not such a worke so great & so substantiall' with the result that the work would only be half done and that, while the result might be satisfactory in a dry season, flooding would occur in the ensuing rainy period for which he would be blamed. What Vermuyden knew was that the scheme which he had designed, if it was to fulfil its purpose, had to be carried out in its entirety and could not be arbitrarily whittled down at the whim of noble Adventurers and their associates whose primary consideration was financial gain. Admittedly a satisfactory financial result was important as this was the main object of the undertaking but Vermuyden knew that an emasculated scheme would achieve nothing except disappointment for all. That he, as possessor of many acres in the

Level, had considerable interest in the financial results is obvious, and his insistent attitude may have been influenced by such consideration, but his determined stand was undoubtedly, and primarily, founded on a professional integrity. Either he was to be responsible for the scheme which he had designed or he would wash his hands of it altogether. And as on the 20th June the Earls of Arundel and Bedford, and the Lord Chief Justice intimated through Sir Edward Partridge and Mr. Fountayne that they agreed with the determination expressed at the meeting on the previous day, there was nothing to be done but to let Sir Cornelius Vermuyden go his way. Nevertheless, there is the feeling that some of the Adventurers had no little regret at this decision.

It is difficult to repress the suspicion that in all these protracted negotiations with Vermuyden, Sir Edward Partridge was one of the main instigators of the hostility towards him. Sir Edward came from Kent and perhaps his first connection with the Fens dates from his appointment as a member of the Committee of the House of Commons on whose findings the Pretended Act was passed. It is to be hoped that during his membership of that Committee he maintained a strict impartiality, but there is no doubt that in due time he was to make quite a good thing out of the Great Level. He eventually went to live at Ely where his house in the College there had nine fireplaces thus indicating from the Hearth Tax Returns that its owner was of some considerable substance.[1] From the time of Partridge's first appearance as an Adventurer at the meeting of the 9th June the opposition against Vermuyden seemed to harden. Added to this, he subsequently put forward his own claim to be made Director of the Works, as will be related later, and, therefore, it is doubtful whether he could at this stage have defended a charge of partiality. Clearly Partridge had no qualifications for drainage work, nor, for that matter, had Sir Miles Sandys, but when the final decision to break with Vermuyden was made these two knights. and Mr. Latch, another Adventurer, were 'desired to call Mr. Glapthorne & Leuieten[t] Coll. Dodson and whome else they may think fitt to show assistance to prepare a Designe of the workes to be done this Summer and to bringe in the same to the Companye with all convenient speede'. Col. Dodson's qualifications we have already discussed. Those of Mr. Glapthorne appear to be only that he was a landowner and had acted as a Commissioner of Sewers in 1629 when Sir Anthony Thomas, John Worsopp, Henry Briggs, and others had endeavoured to be appointed 'undertakers' for the draining of the Great Level.[2] This was the kind of action which

[1] W. M. Palmer, *Camb. Ant. Soc. Proc.* Vol. XXXVIII. 1939.
[2] *Cal. State Paper Dom. Charles I.* CLI[1]. 83.

Vermuyden feared. The appointment of laymen to decide on, and superintend a haphazard and piecemeal programme of work. It was just what he was convinced the proposed 'comptrollment' would involve.

On Friday 22nd June, 'Sir Miles Sandys & Sir Edward Partridge having had the assistance of Mr. Glapthorne and Leiu[tt] Coll. Dodson (according to the order and desire of the Company made on Tueday last) brought in a Designe and estimate in writing of the workes of drayninge thought fitt to be done this Summer which they were desired to leave with the Clarke for the use of the Companye and did accordingly leave the same'. It is not possible to say what this so called 'Designe' involved, but the suspicion is that it was, in fact, no design at all, but merely a brief description and estimate of haphazard work considered immediately essential. Too much emphasis cannot be laid on the futility of such a programme to the dangers of which Vermuyden himself was fully alive. The past history, before 1630, of the so-called draining of the Fens had made this abundantly clear, and a century or so earlier what little co-ordination the great religious houses had been able to exercise in their own domaines, had not, as we know, been sufficient to serve adequately the Fens as a whole. Dodson himself may have had some comprehensive scheme in mind, and even on paper, at this time, and his earlier briefly reported 'Design' of 'setting a Sluce on the River Ouse' may have been a detailed plan. That is conjecture, but we do know that in 1664, long after Vermuyden had disappeared Dodson produced a complete 'Discourse' on similar lines, even if not of similar means, to Vermuyden's, which, though it was never adopted, showed that he had the right idea. Right, at least, from the point of view of appropriate planning. He tells us himself in this 'Discourse', after detailing particulars of his plan, that 'This was the designe, I would have finished in the year 1649, when I was Director'. Possibly that was his intention but possibly also, and more probably, the 'designe' of 1664 evolved in his mind as a comprehensive plan only during the years between 1649 and 1664.

There is little doubt that the Adventurers themselves were beginning to regret somewhat their hasty decision of only a few days earlier that it was 'not fitt to depend upon Sir Cornelius Vermuyden any longer' a regret that was, perhaps, increased by what may have appeared the inadequate proposals of Sandys, Partridge, Glapthorne and Dodson. And so it was recorded of the meeting of only a week later, Friday, 29th June, that 'The Companie takinge into Consideration the necessity of having an able Director for the workes upon debate it was thought fitt and resolved to make some propositions to Sir Cornelius Vermuyden in order to a new Agreement with him if he shall think fitt to make it at Peterborough the 4th July next'.

The Earl of Bedford was present at this meeting, and so was Sir Edward Partridge. Vermuyden was also there. And not only was the above resolution agreed upon, but, in addition, the terms on which the Agreement was to be based were fully minuted. These are of such importance, in view of subsequent happenings, that they warrant full transcription.

1. To give him 4000 acres for his Recompence for perfectinge of the works with such qualifications as shall be thought fitt and agreed.
2. That he shall have his proportion of 4000 acres in such parts of the Levell as shall be adjudged drayned according to the proportion that 4000 acres beareth to 95000 acres in the whole.
3. That he shall have three hundred thyrty three pounds six shillings and eightpence paid for 3 yeares together The said some to be paid to him at the beginning of each yeare.
4. To lymitt the charge of the worke to 95000^{li} in the whole.
5 That if the perfectinge of the worke exceede 95000^{li} then hee to have but 3000 acres And if it exceede 100000^{li} to have [this left blank].

Unfortunately these discussions on the terms of an agreement with Sir Cornelius seem to have gone round and round in a circle as was further evidenced by the minutes of the meeting of the 24th July when the above propositions were enlarged upon.

As far back as the 8th June it had been agreed to give Vermuyden 4,000 acres but now, although this agreement was confirmed, the stipulation was added that he should not dispose of any part of the 4,000 acres until the whole 95,000 acres had been adjudged, and that, also, he should not dispose of more than 2,000 acres for seven years after such adjudication. It is difficult to see now why it was desired to impose these limitations. Certainly Vermuyden saw no justification and in his reply to the earlier offer of the Adventurers, when restrictions of a similar nature had been proposed, he had said that he was prepared to keep the 2,000 acres and that 'my present resolutions are not to part with any part of it neither now or hereafter. But understand I desire to be master of my owne'. A not unnatural desire.

There was still the rather petty matter of the method of payment of the £1,000, but more important it was 'resolved and agreed that if the dreyninge the great Levell of the Fennes shall exceed the some of 90000^{li} then Sir Cornelius Vermuyden shall become an Adventurer and pay all taxes for the 4000 acres untill the charge of dreyninge amounts unto 10000^{li} And if the charge thereof shall exceede the some of 100000^{li} then it shall bee at the choice of Sir Cornelius Vermuyden whether hee will become an Adventurer and pay all Taxes for the 4000 acres proportionable to the rest of the 95000 acres from the tyme of the Acte of Parliament or loose his Recompence'.

What was implied in this was an arbitrary restriction on the total cost of the works. It would have been easy for Vermuyden to accept these conditions and, purely for the sake of safeguarding his own recompense, to have limited expenditure possibly at the cost of the effectiveness of the drainage works. Whatever his other faults it is believed that Vermuyden was sincere in his beliefs. Professional integrity prevailed and not surprisingly 'Sir Cornelius Vermuyden refused to proceede upon their propositions and resolves'.

CHAPTER TWELVE

Default of Adventurers in payment of taxes; consequent lack of capital for undertaking. Vermuyden threatens to petition Parliament. Disaffection of workmen in the Fens.

THE root of all the troubles with which the adventurers were faced was the fact that they were desperately short of money, a fact of which they were well aware, and had indeed discussed at their meeting on 10th July. It had been agreed then that there was an urgent 'necessity of some speedy course to be taken for the raysings of moneys for the present occasion and works of this Summer in regard the tax sett is paid by very few of the Adventurers and participants'. Consequently it was decided that £10,000 should be raised by the sale of 4,000 acres in Peterborough, Crowland and Wisbech at, so the minutes record, '50^{li} per acre'. There is clearly an error in the clerk's entry or in arithmetic here. Undoubtedly the former because on the 8th August it was ordered that Mr. Glapthorne and Col. Dodson should find 'purchasers that will for the 3,991 acres hereunder pay 10,000^{li} vizt. 1,000^{li} downe and 1,000^{li} weekely until the said 10,000^{li} be paid'.

The failure of the individual Adventurers to pay their taxes was a very serious matter and was not confined to the humbler Adventurers. In the minutes of the meeting of the 18th August a list was recorded of the principal defaulters from whom a total sum of £4,577 17s. od. was owing for a combined acreage of 36,628 acres, the list being headed by the Earl of Arundel owing £712, Sir Miles Sandys, the largest debtor, being involved for the sum of £1,153 15s. od. The order was made that, failing payment within a fortnight, the land should be 'forthwith sold.'

The question is, how far did the financial state of the company influence the negotiations with Vermuyden? The answer quite clearly must be that this influence was great. In other words, the Adventurers must have realised that Sir Cornelius Vermuyden, with all his advantageous experience was bound to be a luxury almost beyond their reach. Furthermore, it must have been apparent to them that it was very much in their interests that he should be responsible for the design and execution of the work upon which their fortune depended. Assuming, of course, that they believed that the scheme which Vermuyden had evolved was the right one. Had they this belief? That is a question difficult to answer, but, in spite of the intervention of Westerdyke, it is difficult to conceive that the perseverance, the arrogance if you like, of Sir Cornelius had failed to press home the advantages which he naturally had by virtue of his earlier experience both in Hatfield Chase and in the Great Level itself. Neither of these previous undertakings had been technical failures. That has been emphasised before. In spite of the criticism of Westerdyke on matters of principle there is no denying that Vermuyden's 'Discourse' was a convincing exposition of his plan and it must have had its effect on the Adventurers. But they, men of the world that they were, quite rightly believed in bargaining for what they wanted and their bargaining was made all the harder by the knowledge of the financial straits in which they were. By the same token Vermuyden was perfectly entitled to bargain for the sale of all he had to offer. And that was quite a lot. He was far from being the incubus that Samuel Wells made out. If he had something for sale which was of value to the Adventurers he was quite entitled to negotiate for the highest price. He was no philanthropist, but then nor were the Adventurers and Participants. Nor, for that matter, was Samuel Wells.

The undertaking, was, in truth, woefully under capitalised and everything points to the conclusion that there would have been none of this haggling with Vermuyden if more ample funds had been available. No undertaking of the magnitude of the draining and reclamation of the Great Level could progress satisfactorily when constantly shadowed by an empty exchequer. Colonel Dodson, as noted in the minutes of the meeting of the 24th August, had been appointed 'Assistant under Sir Cornelius' that is if and when any agreement was made with Sir Cornelius. Now Dodson appears to have been sound in his ideas and would likewise appear to have had very similar principles of drainage to those of Vermuyden. Pending any agreement with the latter he was acting as Director, but it was quite impossible for him or any other Director to make any progress or to plan ahead when constantly menaced by the fear that lack of money would produce instructions to stop all work. It was a hand to mouth existence dependent upon vague promises from individuals to pay a hundred pounds or so of outstanding arrears of taxes. Unfulfilled threats of the sale of defaulters' lands did nothing to help. The uncertainty about the fate of the 12,000 acres, a legacy from Charles's undertakings of 1638, was another factor and finally on 12th September at the meeting of the Adventurers the following decision was reached.

'In regard the business of the 12,000 acres is not settled whereby many are discouraged to adventure any moneys and some of the Adventurers to bring in their taxes whereby the work cannot proceed. It is ordered that the workmen be paid and forthwith dismissed until further order.' Sir Cornelius Vermuyden was present at this meeting. What he had to say is not recorded.

Instructions to this effect went forth from London to Col. Dodson in the Fens, but at the same time as these drastic steps were being decided upon it was being agreed again and again to postpone the threatened sale of defaulters' lands. Strength on the one hand, weakness on the other, a vacillating policy which could never pay.

In the meantime a storm was brewing. On 11th September Sir Cornelius had proposed to the Adventurers that the differences which existed between them—and they were not by then of any great magnitude—should be referred to Lord Chief Justice St. John, himself an Adventurer. This sensible proposal was agreed to but it would appear that nothing was done to implement it. On 27th September the storm broke. On that day it was reported that 'Sir Cornelius Vermuyden hath prepared a petition against the Adventurers which he intends to have read in Parliament . . . And that Sir Cornelius Vermuyden hath written to a member of Parliament that the Company intends to prejudice the Navigation of Kings-Lynne. It is therefore ordered that the agreement with Sir Cornelius Vermuyden be from henceforth suspended.'

Of course, as far as the last sentence is concerned, no agreement with Sir Cornelius had been reached but, apart from that, there seems little, if anything, to justify what appear to be somewhat underhand methods on the part of Vermuyden. From what has been said much earlier in this book it will be realised that no attempt has been made to present the character of Vermuyden in any pleasant light. Our conclusions have, indeed, been very much in the other direction but, in this particular instance, there is the evidence of only one side and there may have been a point of view other than that presented by the minutes of the Company. In any minute book, as has been quoted before, 'the clerk doth in discretion forbear to enter many things spoken'. If Vermuyden had been working in close harmony with the rest of the Adventurers there would have been no possible excuse for what might have seemed to them a stab in the back. We know, however, that a constant state of friction prevailed and the minutes of the meetings tell us nothing of the protests which Vermuyden may have raised against the methods of draining which the Company had apparently decided to adopt pending any decision as to his employment as Director of the works. We should be the last to suggest that Vermuyden was a mild, peaceable and straightforward individual of whom the Adventurers took advantage. If any advantage was to be taken we should be inclined to put the odds on Sir Cornelius, but that does not destroy the fact that ever since the passing of the Pretended Act he had had a lot to put up with. He had seen the Adventurers see-saw from one decision to another. He had seen, what he considered, a lot of amateurs hoping to dictate to him how the Great Level should be drained. He had seen the Earl of Bedford go behind his back and discuss his scheme with Westerdyke. He had seen the pathetic penury of the undertaking leading to the whittling down of the works and this he knew would in the end be its destruction. What final foolishness had led him to the extreme step of presenting, or intending to present, a petition to Parliament we do not know, but if there was something in the scheme which was in his opinion prejudicial to the navigation of King's Lynn, then that scheme must have been very different from what he himself had proposed to the Adventurers.

Vermuyden's action appears, on paper, to have little to justify it but we would prefer not to condemn him solely on the evidence of the one side.

But these expressions of indignation at Sir Cornelius Vermuyden's conduct did nothing to help the health of the undertaking. On 11th October the Clerk was once more instructed 'to write several letters to the Adventurers underwritten to pay in their of arreres of both paymente of the taxe of 2s. 6d. per acre', the text of the clerk's letter being as follows: 'At a meeting of the Adventurers of the 11th of this moneth I was commanded by them to acquaint you they have lately received letters from Colo.ll Castell & Leiften, Colo.ll Dodson that for want of money to pay the workmen they fall into mutinies and seize upon the officers and threaten to carry them away and cutt them in pieces, in case they have not speedy payment. And that divers of the Adventurers have already paid both their payments of the taxe of 2s. 6d. per acre & some more They therefore desire you for the preventing of this great mischiefe and to preserve the reputation and honor of the Company speedily to make payment to the Treasurer of your proportion of the said Taxe in arrere.'

That letter gives some idea of the conditions in the Fens themselves while the Adventurers in London, or those few who condescended to attend the meetings, expressed unfulfilled threats of sale against their defaulting associates. But perhaps Vermuyden's decisive and unpopular attitude had stung them into some kind of action because on 2nd October they had 'Ordered that Thursday the 8th November next be appointed a peremptory day for the sale of all such of the Adventurers and participants lands which have not paid their money . . . and evrie defaulter is to take notice thereof at his perill.'

As events were to prove, this time they meant business and on the 8th November the sale of defaulters lands was actually, if somewhat half-heartedly, begun.

Prior to this date, on 27th October, in spite of the indignant resolutions expressed at the meeting of 27th September 'it was putt to the question whether Sir Cornelius Vermuyden should be director or not and resolved in the affirmative' and it was agreed that, as Vermuyden had proposed on 11th September, the differences between him and the Company should be referred to the Lord Chief Justice St. John. A complete change of face which, however, as events were to prove, was not to be the last.

Now this book does not set out to be a history of the Corporation of the Bedford Level from the time of the passing of the Pretended Act in 1649. That result could best be achieved by transcribing in full the minutes of the meetings from that date. What we are concerned about in those minutes is only those entries which help to an understanding of the part played by Sir Cornelius Vermuyden in the development of the undertaking. We are not, at the moment concerned with the technical side of the undertaking. That will come later, but summing up at this comparatively early stage of the development we feel that enough has been said, enough of the minutes transcribed, and nothing relevant has been suppressed, to sustain the contention that Vermuyden had been somewhat sorely tried. If he had told the Adventurers, politely or impolitely, that he had no further interest in their undertaking, nobody could have blamed him. Undoubtedly he did not do this because he himself had too much at stake in the Great Level, but it must not be overlooked that whenever a breach occurred it was the Company that made the move to heal it, not Vermuyden.

CHAPTER THIRTEEN

Anthony Hammond's proposals on behalf of Sir Edward Partridge; their acceptance. Vermuyden demonstrates futility of proposals. Agreement with Vermuyden finally signed.

And so we come now to the final act in this human comedy, this clash of vital personalities, the act which was to end not so much in what Wells perhaps rather facetiously termed the triumph of Sir Cornelius Vermuyden, but in his complete justification. At least, that is the considered judgement of the present writer and if he may be accused of showing bias in his approach to that judgement the excuse lies in acceptance of G. M. Trevelyan's statement that 'Since history is our interpretation of human affairs in the past, it could not exist without bias'.[1] But, as he goes on to say, 'God gives us a true bias.'

There is no desire or intention to disparage in any way the actions of the Earl of Bedford and his fellow Adventurers. Theirs was a difficult position. In spite of their previous brave and defiant decision to have nothing more to do with Sir Cornelius Vermuyden, in their hearts they felt that there was no one possessing the specialised knowledge or the experience of the energetic Dutchman. And for this reason it was that they were continually changing their minds. There was too much at stake to warrant their abandoning completely Vermuyden and all he stood for. But their decision of 27th September to approach him once more was not forced upon them against their wills solely because Vermuyden had the whip hand. He had much more than that. He had something to offer which was of extreme value. And the Adventurers were fully aware of this fact.

What happened after the meeting of 27th October, is a little obscure. Whether or not the Adventurers were too occupied with the question of putting pressure on for the collection of taxes, and the minutes of their meetings certainly show that the measures decided upon were being energetically enforced, the fact remains that a month elapsed before, on Monday 26th November, any mention is again made of Sir Cornelius Vermuyden.

[1] *History*. Vol. XXXII. No. 115. 1947.

On that day it was 'Ordered that Mr. Gorges be desired forthwith to conferre with Sir Cornelius Vermuyden that he may bring in his final demands to the Company on Thursday next that the business betweene the Company and him may be put to a final conclusion'. What Vermuyden's reactions were to that proposal nobody knows. He was not present at the meeting, but to suggest that final demands should once more be submitted, seems to indicate a desire to prolong indefinitely the negotiations which had continued for so long and so fruitlessly. When, on 27th October, the decision had been reached to refer the differences to the Lord Chief Justice, it had also been ordered that Sir Cornelius Vermuyden should 'in convenient tyme enter his consent in the Clerk's booke to be likewise bound' by the Lord Chief Justice's decision. Seeing that the suggestion for this arbitration had come originally from Vermuyden himself it seems to have been somewhat unnecessary to stipulate that he should signify his agreement to this course in the Clerk's book. This opinion was, apparently, held by Vermuyden because, when the meeting on Thursday was held, attended by the large number of nineteen Adventurers, it was recorded that he had not entered his consent and, therefore, the Company was, 'at large as well as Sir Cornelius and not further bound thereby'. In spite of this Mr. Gorges, Mr. Hammond, Mr. Castell, Mr. Henley and Mr. Latch were desired 'to attend the Lord Chief Justice St. John touching the differences betweene the Company and Sir Cornelius Vermuyden'. Sir Cornelius was present at this meeting and his comments might conceivably have been somewhat illuminating.

That he did, however, once more state his 'final' demands is apparent from the minutes of the meeting of 7th December when he delivered in these demands in writing and stated emphatically that he would not recede in any way from them, a course of conduct which the Company considered unreasonable. What Sir Cornelius thought of the Company's attitude is not recorded.

Possibly their attitude was based on the false hope, that there was another course open to them, and possibly likewise, there had been some lobbying on the part of Mr. Anthony Hammond before the meeting because it was he who informed the Company 'that for 30,000^{li} a gentleman will give Caution of 4,000^{li} for the drayninge of that part of the great level which lyeth betweene Bedford river and Welland according to the Act of Parliament'. The 'Gentleman' was none other than Sir Edward Partridge who with unnecessary modesty had been absent from the meeting when Mr. Hammond had made his anonymous proposition. But on the following day, 8th December, Sir Edward came out into the open with the proposition 'that for 30,000^{li} to be paid at King's Lynne, Wisbech or Peterborough by

5,000[li] per mensem the first payment to be made on the 10th day of January next beside what moneys are already disbursed and making use of such tymber and materials as are already bought hee will undertake to drayne the north part of the great levell of the Fennes lying betweene Bedford River and Welland and within one year next ensuing to performe the same Worke according to the Act of Parliament.'

Well, there was the proposal and on the face of it it does not seem to have offered any more than was contained in Sir Cornelius's proposals, because for £30,000 Sir Edward was prepared to drain only about one-third of the Great Level, and the easiest third too, when Vermuyden demanded about £100,000 for draining the whole of the Level. Furthermore, it must not be overlooked that Sir Edward only proposed to do the work on paper. He had no experience, he had no scheme. In fact the whole thing appears to have been a stupendous piece of bluff put forward by one who truly merited the title 'adventurer'. Or was he, perhaps, working in collusion with his fellow Adventurers in the hope of forcing Vermuyden's hand? Fortunately on this occasion we have some indication of Vermuyden's opinion because it was recorded that when Mr. Henley, one of his ardent supporters, suggested that there were other propositions, including Vermuyden's to be considered, 'Sir Cornelius being present declared to the Company that hee utterly disclaymed to meddle or have anything to doe with the dreyning of the Fens'. Behind that bare report lies a wealth of bitter feeling and, doubtless, outspoken comment.

Robert Henley was no fool. Nor, apparently, was he considered so by his fellow adventurers as in June they had elected him Treasurer to the Company in succession to the Earl of Bedford who 'could not with convenience perform the place'. His confidence in Sir Cornelius Vermuyden was so strong that at the next meeting on 10th December he 'offered to the Company that if Sir Cornelius Vermuyden be director of the Worke hee will engage 4,000 acres which he hath already and 4,000 acres more which he hath and will purchase, that Sir Cornelius shall with or under the charge of 109,700[li] to the Company vizt. 33,500[li] for the north part of Bedford River and 76,200[li] for the south side thereof doe the worke according to the Act of Parliament'. A practical proof of his faith, but, without going further into the details of the discussions which took place during those fateful days, it is enough to say that on the afternoon of 12th December, 1649, 'the question being putt whether Sir Cornelius Vermuyden or Sir Edward Partridge should be the Director of the Worke', twelve of the Adventurers present voted for the latter and two only, Mr. Henley and Mr. Ingram, voted for Sir Cornelius. The Earl of Bedford was not present at this meeting so that we do not know what his feelings were. With such an overwhelming vote there was no alternative but to accept Sir Edward Partridge's proposition and this was done 'nemine contradicente', as recorded in the minutes.

Had this decision remained, and we know, of course that it did not, the 12th December, 1649, might have been a baleful day for the Great Level of the Fens. It might have meant the end of Vermuyden's practical work there and it would be interesting to speculate what other work he might have engaged on in order to satisfy his restless energy. Possibly he might have turned his attention then to the drainage of Sedgmoor, but quite clearly the result would have been his comparative extinction as a drainage engineer, as on his work in the Great Level his reputation must stand or fall. And what of the Great Level itself? What would have been its fate? That depends upon the nature of the scheme of drainage which Sir Edward Partridge intended to carry out. There is no evidence in existence to indicate what this might have been. Indeed, as events were to show, it is doubtful whether any well defined scheme ever existed and Sir Edward would appear to have been more concerned with the financial gain from his proposed operations than with any sound practical considerations on which the operations were to be based. No doubt Colonel Dodson would have been employed on the practical work but while he may have later developed, as has been suggested earlier, ideas and principles not very dissimilar from those of Vermuyden, that development was some years ahead and resulted directly from his association with Vermuyden. In 1649 he was sufficiently opposed to Sir Cornelius to vote against him at the meeting of 12th December. Was this perhaps a triumph of political expediency over professional conviction?

It was not long, however, before the futility of Partridge's proposals became apparent, or rather, were made apparent by Sir Cornelius himself, because this was the one occasion on which the importance of the issue induced him to make the first move towards a reversal of a decision reached at a meeting of the Company. Vermuyden undoubtedly desired himself to be the Director of the Work, but it is felt that the impulse which decided him to take this course was not solely self interest, but more the firm conviction that there was nothing in Partridge's plan, if he could be said to have had a plan, to show that it would work. And thus at the meeting of 1st January, 1649–50 he offered to demonstrate to the Earl of Bedford the Lord Chief Justice St. John, Sir Miles Sandys, Sir Edward Partridge, Mr. Henley and Mr. Latch that 'Sir Edward Parterich his designe is destructive to the work of drayning in diverse particulars', a challenge which had to be

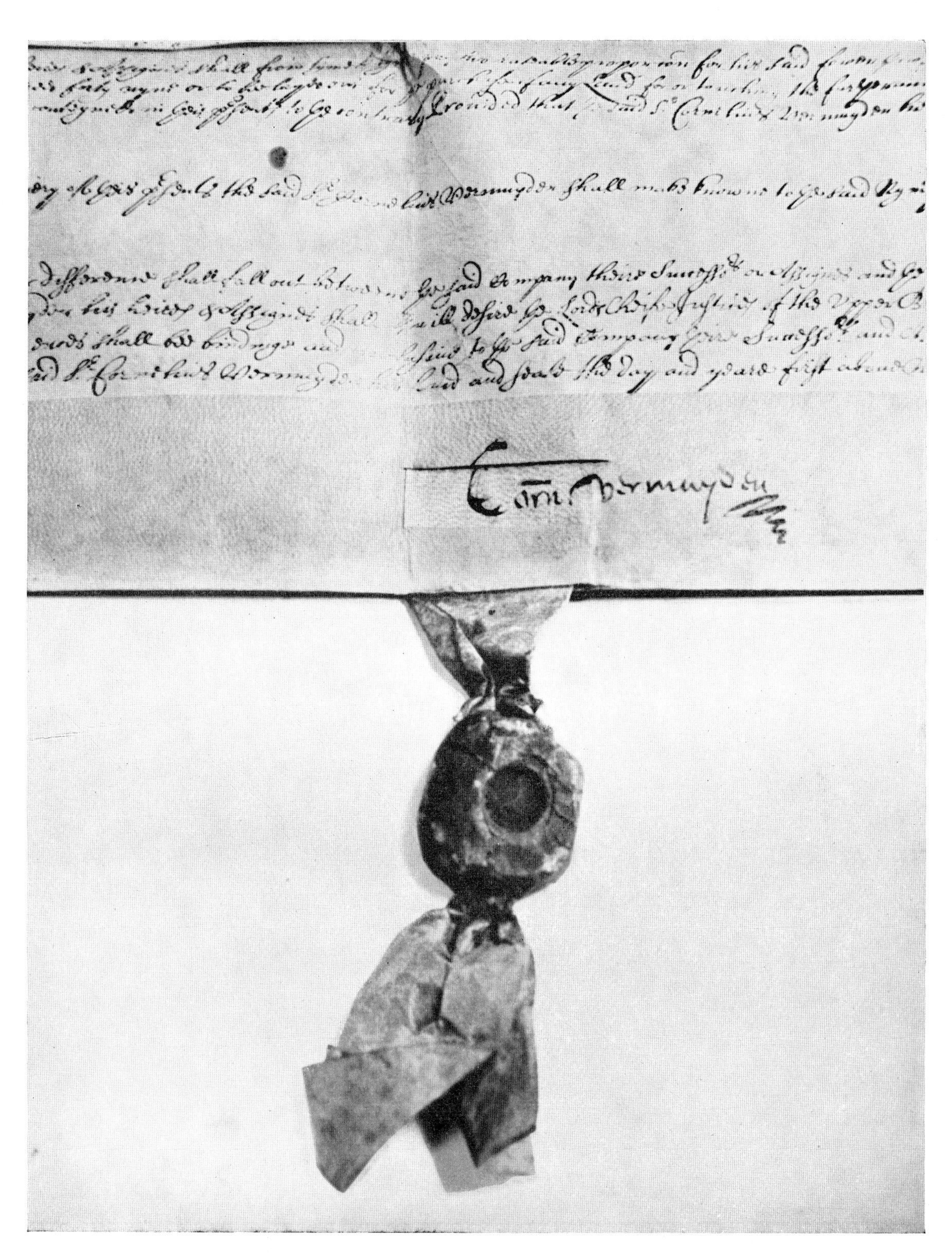

Plate VI. Vermuyden's Signature on the Agreement of 25 January, 1649/50.

accepted. Consequently it was ordered that Sir Cornelius should make his demonstration the following morning at nine o'clock.

And that was the end of Sir Edward Partridge as far as his pretensions to being Director of the work of draining were concerned. There were meetings of the Company on 2nd and 10th January in the minutes of which no mention occurs of this question of the rival claims of the two would-be-Directors, but at the next meeting on 24th January, 'A draught of Articles of Agreement betweene the Company and Sir Cornelius Vermuyden touching his being Director of the Work of drayning was read and upon the reading thereof assented unto and agreed as well by the Company as by Sir Cornelius Vermuyden'. At this meeting his design was given official approval. On 25th January, 1649–50 that agreement was signed by Sir Cornelius Vermuyden 'in the presence of Geo. Glapthorne, Jo. Thurloe, Geo. Smith, John Hampson, Wm. Palmer'.

Impartially examined this agreement shows nothing in the nature of a 'triumph' for Sir Cornelius. A copy is still preserved in the Fen Office at Ely with Vermuyden's determined signature at the foot and had Samuel Wells himself made an impartial examination he could have shown that Vermuyden, far from gaining all that he had demanded so determinedly, eventually signed a document which gave to the Corporation of the Bedford Level all, or nearly all, for which they had stood out. Instead Wells preferred to make no reference at all to the terms of the contract.

Vermuyden abandoned his resistance to the supervision of the work from the Adventurers and agreed 'to . . . bee subject to and observe such orders and directions in and about the draynings aforesaid conducinge to the furtherance thereof as hee shall receive from the nyne persons appointed by the order of the said Company on the tenth of January'. He accepted the placing of control of the 2,000 acres of the 4,000 to be allotted to him in the hands of 'Feoffees or trustees' for a period of seven years, he agreed to the payment of his one thousand pounds by three hundred pounds down and the balance at the rate of twenty pounds per month, and he accepted the limit of £100,000 on the expenditure of the work of draining subject to certain penalties to be imposed on him should the sum be exceeded. If these clauses are compared with what Vermuyden had stood out for at the meeting of 19th June, 1649, it will be clear that he gave way all along the line and that, if anybody triumphed, it was the Company and not he.

To say that from the time of the signing of this agreement everything from Vermuyden's point of view was plain sailing would be far from the truth. He had all too many obstacles to overcome, but there is little evidence in the Proceedings to show that he had any serious clashes with the

Adventurers themselves such as were so frequent in the early months of the resumed undertaking which preceded his final appointment as Director. It is understandable that by many the confirmation of Sir Cornelius in his appointment was accepted with a bad grace. The overwhelming majority against him in the voting at the meeting of 12th December makes this perfectly clear and even if the individual Adventurers knew that for the sake of their own fortunes support for Vermuyden was imperative, yet, no doubt human nature sometimes prevailed to the hindrance of his work. It is doubtful, for example, if Sir Edward Partridge ever considered Sir Cornelius Vermuyden as one of his close friends. But, as far as can be read from the Proceedings, Vermuyden did not have much occasion to complain of what he had so feared in the initial stages, undue 'comptrollment' of his work. Or perhaps he himself was more complaisant.

The question of the comparison of the work which Vermuyden completed in the Great Level with what he originally laid down in the 'Discourse' will be discussed in some detail later on, particularly in relation to the cut-off channel and flood relief channel, neither of which, in fact, were ever carried out. But now it can be asked, who was responsible for the omission of these important details? Was it Vermuyden or was it the Adventurers themselves?

At a meeting held on 25th January, 1649–50, it was reported that, 'According to a clause in the Articles of Agreement betweene the Company and Sir Cornelius Vermuyden the Company for theire approbation and upon debate and consideration thereof his designe was approved of in the general being considered by the Company present a probable way to effect the Work of drayning according to the Act of Parliament'. It is as well here to note the cautious expression of opinion of the 'probability' of the design being suitable. What was that design? Eleven years had passed since the 'Discourse' had been first written and seven since its publication. How far had Vermuyden receded from his original principles? To what extent had he trimmed his sails to placate the hostile elements among the Adventurers? Had he, in order to meet their demands for reduced costs, jettisoned the all-important features of the cut-off and flood relief channels? Nobody can tell, but it is difficult to believe that Vermuyden, with his clear insight into the problems of the Great Level, as is evidenced by the 'Discourse' itself, would have consented to an emasculated scheme even in order to oust his rivals, and notably Sir Edward Partridge. Whatever the explanation, the fact remains that the 'Discourse' tells us clearly what he knew should be done, and the Great Level itself shows us what he was permitted to do.

CHAPTER FOURTEEN

Final adjudication obtained. Consultation with Westerdyke again suggested. Vermuyden leaves Adventurers' service. His relations with Cromwell. Malvern Chase. Proposals for draining Sedgmoor. Accusations against Vermuyden.

THE story of the undertaking from the time of the signing of the agreement with Vermuyden in January 1649–50 is given in some detail by Wells[1] and there is no need to repeat it here. The first adjudication was obtained on 24th March, 1650 (old stype) when the commissioners 'adjudged all that part of the said Great Levell of the Fennes lying on the north-west part of Bedford River to be dreyned in such sort as by the acte of parliament is appointed to be dreyned; amountinge in the whole to one hundred and seventy thousand acres or thereabouts', and the Adventurers were allotted fifty-eight thousand two hundred acres, their proportion of the ninety-five thousand acres due on completion of the whole undertaking. Two years later, at a meeting of the Adventurers on 17th February, 1652–53 it was recorded that 'Sir Cornelius Vermuyden . . . in performance of the contracts made with the Companie as Director of the works, does hereby declare, that the works concerning the whole remaynder of the Great Level of the Fennes unadjudged are now finished'. On 26th March, 1653, the final adjudication was granted and the Earl of Bedford and his fellow Adventurers entered into possession of the whole of their 95,000 acres. But that, far from being the end of the undertaking, as everybody hoped, was, indeed, only the beginning of a perilous adventure, unconcluded to this very day, and of a story with which Sir Cornelius Vermuyden, and, therefore, this book, are not concerned.

The discourse which Vermuyden read over to the Lords Commissioners at the time of this second adjudication was really an explanation of the means which he had adopted for the draining of the South Level and his reasoning on the causes of flooding in the Level. As far as the North and Middle Levels were concerned he was on safe ground in asserting that there

[1] *op. cit.*

were 'about 40,000 acres at this time sowne with cole seed, wheate, and other winter graine . . .' which had not been 'surrounded' for two years, or since the first adjudication. That was a fact which was patent to all and provided, in fact, ample justification for Vermuyden and his 'design' as far as the North and Middle Levels were concerned. As to the causes of flooding in the South Level no fault can be found with his statement that the Level was 'watered by five rivers which ran through it, and did heretofore occasion the surrounding thereof, namely, the river Ouze, the river of Grant, the river of Mildenhall, the river of Brandon, and the river of Stoake'. In other words as we should say today, the Ouse, the Cam, the Lark, the Little Ouse, and the Wissey. That was the conclusion at which he had arrived in 1638 when he wrote his 'Discourse' but although then he had considered it necessary to provide the cut-off channel for the last four of the rivers to prevent them discharging into the Ouse between Earith and Salter's Lode, by 1653 he had abandoned the cut-off channel and endeavoured to avert the danger of flooding by the provision of 'sufficient bankes, leaving proportionable receptacles between the said bankes for any sudden downfall'. Perhaps he thought that by the provision of the New Bedford, or Hundred Foot, River he was safe in dispensing with the cut-off channel. Or again he may have abandoned this last feature to meet the wishes of those Adventurers whose cry was 'expend not so much.'

At the time of this second adjudication, while the results obtained in the North and Middle Levels had been proved over a period of two years, the South Level was still in the problematical stage with no evident results, only the prophetical optimism of Sir Cornelius Vermuyden. Time was to show that this optimism was not entirely justified, but in 1653 and the ensuing two years this fact had not been clearly demonstrated, although there is clear evidence that there was, at least, some doubt on the part of certain Adventurers as to whether all was well with Vermuyden's work. Which leads us back to our old friend, or shall we say, Vermuyden's old enemy, Westerdyke, for at a meeting of the Company held at Mr. Henley's house 'without Temple Barre' on 4th April, 1655, it was agreed 'that the Company be desired to take into consideration att their next general meetinge the employinge of Mr. Barance Westerdyke for his advice direction and assistance touchinge the Great Levell and allowing him a fitt recompence for the same. In the mean tyme Col. Sam Jones is desired to speak with Mr. Vandeput . . . to write to the said Barance Westerdyke to know if the Company had a mynde to send for him whether or no he will come to them for the purpose aforesaid and how long hee will stay and what reward hee will demand either by the month quarter or year.'

Whether Westerdyke ever came over in response to the invitation sent him by Mr. Vandeput we do not know but whatever happened it was of little account to Sir Cornelius Vermuyden unless, of course, Westerdyke was the cause of his disappearance, because on 4th February following, that is still 1655 by the old reckoning, he attended his last meeting of the Company. There is no explanation in the Proceedings on the reason for, or the manner of, his going. There is no recognition of his services to the Company. His name never appears again in their records except that, in the minutes of the meeting on the following day, the 5th February, there is a mention of 'the 2,000 acres of Sir Cornelius Vermuyden which are to remain in the Trustee's hands for 7 years'. The curtain falls, and, as far as the Company of Adventurers is concerned, Sir Cornelius Vermuyden ceases to exist.

And then arises one of the eternal questions in the Vermuyden story. Did Westerdyke come over in 1655, and was his verdict so unfavourable, as it undoubtedly was bound to be, knowing, as we do, his antagonism to Vermuyden, that the Adventurers decided at last to dispense with Vermuyden? Our opinion is that he did not nor are we prepared to accept the vindictive statement of Samuel Wells that the failure of Sir Cornelius to account for a sum of money that had been entrusted to him for the works was the direct cause of his departing.[1] So far we have found no documentary proof for this accusation. It may be that Vermuyden quarrelled with the Earl of Bedford or the much simpler explanation may be that he decided himself that his work in the Level was ended and that he desired to devote himself to fresh pursuits. There is nothing whatever to justify the conclusion, hinted at by Wells, that he left the Company of Adventurers in disgrace.

Oliver Cromwell as Lord Protector had given every support and encouragement to the Earl of Bedford and his co-Adventurers in the Great Level which is, perhaps, confirmatory testimony to the opinion which we have expressed earlier that it was not the drainage of the Fens itself to which he objected in 1638, but to the terms of the adjudication granted to Francis, Earl of Bedford. We have also suggested that at that time there may have existed some form of friendship between Sir Cornelius Vermuyden and Cromwell, and it would seem as if, by the year 1653, that friendship had expanded into something of a more confidential nature. Gardiner tells us that 'on September 23 1653 one of Cromwell's confidants—probably Sir Cornelius Vermuyden, the drainer of the Fens—carried to Van de Perre the most astounding proposals ever made by an Englishman to the minister of a foreign State'.[2] These so-called 'astounding proposals' were the sug-

[1] *Op cit.* Vol. I, p. 288.

[2] S. R. Gardiner, *History of the Commonwealth and Protectorate*, 1897. 349–51.

gested terms of a treaty between England and the States General, but it would appear from the details which Birch gives in the State Papers of Thurloe[1] that, while the proposals in question were definitely made by Sir Cornelius Vermuyden, and he quotes the paper in full, it is not clear that they were, indeed, made direct either to Van de Perre or to Beveringh, the Dutch Ambassador in London at the time. It is quite possible that the proposals were made only to Cromwell for his consideration. These were for 'a perpetual amity between England and the Netherlands and that they take up arms offensive and defensive jointly against the enemy of both states'! The proposed treaty provided also for the parcelling up of Asia and South America between the United Provinces and England, regardless, apparently, of the feelings of the other nations. These proposals were certainly novel, undoubtedly ambitious, and might quite easily have emanated from the enterprising mind of Sir Cornelius Vermuyden. And then in 1655 one John Vermuyden, sent a letter to the Protector dealing with the question of relations with Sweden, and the treaty with that country signed on 11th April, 1654, as affected by the abdication of the Queen of Sweden in favour of her nephew. Some of the conclusions in this letter were based on the possibility of an invasion of the Netherlands by the Swedish forces, and details are given of how such a possibility might be affected by the topographical and geographical features of Friesland. The letter is dated 'Dorchester House, the 16th of July, 1655' and finishes with the following postscript:

I am to goe out of towne on Tuesday next; so that I had not above 1½ houres time for the writing of this. I humbly crave pardon for the folly, no one knowing of it–.[2]

John Vermuyden might have been the son of Sir Cornelius born in 1629, and, therefore, twenty-six years of age at the time, but the more likely identification is with Sir Cornelius's nephew Johan, son of his brother Bartel, who had been born at St. Maartensdijk in 1595, and, who certainly had worked for a time with his uncle on the drainage of the Great Level. Johan is said to have left England and returned to the Netherlands sometime before 1651, and had settled down in his house which he built at Schakerloo, between Tholen and St. Maartensdijk, 'Het Huys Vermuyden', which still stands today. He was certainly qualified to supply the information contained in the letter to the Protector and the postscript to this might indicate that in writing it he was conveying the meaning that, not only was he to 'goe out of towne', but was returning to the Netherlands.

Apart from any personal relationships there is plenty of evidence to show

[1] THOMAS BIRCH, *A Collection of State Papers of John Thurloe Esq.* 1742, ii. 125.

[2] THOMAS BIRCH, *A Collection of State Papers of John Thurloe Esq.* Vol. III, p. 652. 1742.

that the link between the Company of Adventurers and the Protector and his Council was quite strong. Cromwell himself does not appear personally in any of the Company's records but, for example, among those attending the meetings in and around 1655 is to be found the name of Commissary-General Edward Whalley, the notorious regicide. All this, and the evidence of earlier years in the history of the drainage of the Great Level, points to a close connection between Sir Cornelius and Oliver Cromwell and it is quite credible that the former, in company with his nephew Johan, was working for the Protector on, what might be termed, intelligence matters connected with the Netherlands.

But what, clearly, Sir Cornelius hoped for after he left the service of the Adventurers in 1655 was that he would be able to direct his energies to the drainage of the 4,000 acres of Sedgmoor purchased from the Crown in 1630 and still remaining in his possession. That hope, however, as he was eventuall to discover, was never to be fulfilled. Undoubtedly when he had purchased this land in Sedgmoor, and at the same time an area of Malvern Chase, Vermuyden had taken the view that eventually both these areas, of little value in their virgin state, could be improved into profitable investments by enclosing, disafforesting and draining. But to say, as has been done so often in the past, that Vermuyden drained both Sedgmoor and Malvern Chase is quite untrue and such statements are merely based on the assumption that, having purchased a piece of waste land, he immediately drained it. That might have been his intention but intention and performance are two very different things.

As far as Malvern Chase is concerned the story of Vermuyden's purchase, and the subsequent developments, is an extremely complicated one to which it has not yet been possible to find a definite conclusion. The whole question of the ownership by the Crown of the Chase, and the rights which went with that ownership, is itself a very complicated one into which we need not enter here. The essential document in our story is a Privy Signet dated August 1630 which comprised 'A Warrant to the Lord Treasurer to conclude a Contract on His Majesty's behalf with Sir Cornelius Vermuyden for the Forrest or Chace of Malverne . . .'[1] to be followed in October of the same year by instructions to the Attorney-General, Sir Robert Heath, 'to prepare a bill ready for our signature, to be passed under our privy seal' confirming the purchase of the King's portion of the chase for the sum of £5,000, £4,000 of which, incidentally, was to be paid 'unto Philip Burla-

[1] For this, and further information, I am indebted to Mr. H. H. Foster, Clerk to the Malvern Hills Conservators, and to Mr. E. H. Sargeant, County Archivist, Worcester.

machi Esq. as discharge of debts by us owing unto him'.[1] On 10th March, 1631–2 the Forest was disafforested by Letters Patent under the Great Seal, but considerable difficulties were encountered by the Commissioners appointed to enclose the one-third allotted to the Crown, that portion which had been disposed of to Vermuyden.[2] A further difficulty was the opposition from Sir Thomas Russell who had held the office of Forester of the Chase and who, naturally, was somewhat disgruntled at the change of ownership and its consequence to him. It is quite clear that during all these difficult negotiations Sir Robert Heath was of the greatest assistance to Sir Cornelius Vermuyden and, indeed, may have had some interest with him in the financial side of the business, in spite of his own official position. But from the rather meagre and conflicting evidence available it would appear that Vermuyden realised that he had not found a profitable investment and soon disposed of his interest, because we learn from a Patent Roll of 12th July, 1637 that the land of Malvern Chase 'formerly granted to Sir Cornelius Vermuyden' was granted to Sir William Russell and George Strode at a fee farm rent of £10 per annum. Furthermore, from a document of 1664, there is evidence to show that the land came into the possession of 'Sir Nicholas Strode of the Inner Temple, London, knight'.[3] When Vermuyden disposed of his interest cannot yet be stated, but what is definite is that he never drained Malvern Chase.

Sedgmoor, however, is an entirely different matter. Equally, Vermuyden never carried out drainage operations there, but that was not due to any lack of effort on his part, and the whole story is much more fully documented so that we can gain a clear idea of the whole course of events. At the time of his purchase of the 4,000 acres there in 1630 Vermuyden must have known that some ten years previously, in 1620 or 1621, James I had seriously contemplated the enclosing and draining of the whole of Sedgmoor, possession of which, amounting to some 12,000 acres, had come to the Crown from the Abbey of Glastonbury on the dissolution. This proposal of the King's was far from unpopular with the Lords of the Manors bordering on Sedgmoor and they had, indeed, presented a petition to James in the following terms.

'As you have made known to us your purpose of having the moor drained, that some good part of it might be converted to your use, and the rest improved for those who have the right of common, allotting each of us a proportion, we thank you therefor, and beseech you to accept 4,000 acres,

[1] *State Papers Dom. Series Car. I*, Vol. 174. No. 1, 1 Oct., 1630.
[2] *Malvern Hills, Historical Sketch*, MS in County Record Office, Worcs.
[3] *An Act of Confirmation of the Inclosure and Improvement of Malvern Chace*, 1664.

and grant us the residue in fee simple, to be used in common as before, debarring all intruders, whereby we believe our allotment will be more profitable than our common over the whole moor has been.'[1] James was graciously pleased to accept this offer from the Lords of the Manors and gave orders to the Exchequer officers and to the Attorney-General to issue the necessary commissions and the requisite deeds for the grant to the tenants of their portions. But, as in the case of the Great Level, James was distracted from his purpose by the pressure of more urgent outside events and in 1625 died before all these necessary preliminaries could be completed.

With this knowledge of all these facts Vermuyden must have been confident when he purchased the 4,000 acres from Charles that he would have little difficulty in obtaining the necessary authority to carry out the drainage of Sedgmoor. But if extraneous circumstances had baulked James of his purpose, Sir Cornelius had had to contend with many more obstructive elements to deprive him of his intended plan. In 1630 he could hardly have been expected to foresee all the complications of Hatfield Chase, the long years of the Civil War, and the difficulties of the Great Level. In 1655, with all these distractions behind him, it was not unreasonable to expect that he might now be permitted to carry out the work which was to benefit not only himself but the several tenants of the wastes of Sedgmoor.

It was on 29th August, 1655 that Sir Cornelius addressed a petition to the Protector relating the facts concerning the proposed draining of Sedgmoor in James's reign, his own purchase of the 4,000 acres from the Crown in the reign of Charles and praying for a new commission to be appointed 'to set out indifferently for petitioner the 4,000 acres that he may go on with so good a work', for, as he said, he 'will be ruined if deprived of his right, long since purchased at a deare rate'. It would appear that the Attorney-General had reported in favour of the proposal in February, 1654, at least on the legality of the renewal of the commission, and Sir Cornelius could with some justification have felt optimism on the outcome of his petition.[2] The general feeling of the Lords of the Manors was still favourable as evidenced by the letter written to Vermuyden by one of them, Ralph Horsey, on 30th October, 1655.

I have received notice that you are going about the enclosure of Sedgmoor. I am glad of it, and you shall have my best assistance. I hope we shall have the allowance agreed on for our manor of Horsey. I will give my assent under my hand. Present my love and service to your lady.[3]

[1] *Cal. State Paper Dom. 1655*. Vol. C., p. 302.
[2] *Cal. State Paper Dom. 1655*. Vol. C. 301, 302.
[3] *Ibid.* 1655–56. Vol. CXXVII. 57 III. 337/8.

But soon the brightness of these hopes was to be somewhat dimmed by a cloud that appeared on the horizon, a cloud which, if it did not itself destroy the prospects, may have had some bearing on the ultimate outcome. On 23rd January, 1655/6 a petition was presented to the Protector by Captain Henry Thornton and Edward King, merchant of London, in which they accused Vermuyden of fraud in connection with his claim to the 4,000 acres of Sedgmoor, in that, as they stated, while he had purchased the land from Charles for £12,000 he had, with the connivance of Sir Robert Heath paid only £6,000.[1]

This episode provides another of the uncertainties of the Vermuyden story. Unfortunately there is nothing to show whether there was any truth in, or outcome of, the allegation. We do not even know who Thornton and King were, but while there may have been something in this story it must be realised that it would be easy for an unscrupulous enemy to make an accusation of this nature, however untrue it might be, in the hope that some of the mud would stick. Sir Cornelius Vermuyden and Sir Robert Heath had been, as we know, friends and close associates in many ventures and if it were desired to be uncharitable, it might be said that, according to the morality of the times, a deal such as that insinuated in the petition could have been far from improbable.

Whatever the outcome of any inquiries into this accusation, if, indeed, they were ever made, the Committee of the Council appear to have been uninfluenced because on 27th May, 1656, they ordered that the matter of Sir Cornelius's petition be proceeded with,[2] and in doing this they were certainly taking into consideration the favourable replies which had been received from the Lords of the Manors, whom they had circularised some months earlier, and whose opinion was generally similar to that indicated in Ralph Horsey's letter to Vermuyden.

On Saturday, 27th December, 1656, Major General Packer introduced into Parliament 'A Bill, touching dividing of a common [Sedgmoor] for Sir Cornelius Vermeudon, with the consent of the freeholders and Commoners', but 'Mr. Bond, affirmed that the tenants and freeholders did not consent. Whereupon the Bill was rejected.'[3]

From this brief entry, and from what has been related before, it can be concluded that, even if the Lords of the Manors favoured the enclosing and draining of Sedgmoor, the opposition which finally wrecked the Bill came from the small commoners, thus providing a case in parallel with all those

[1] *Cal. State Paper Dom. Commonwealth 1655/6.* 64.
[2] *Cal. State Paper. Dom. 1655–56.* CXXVII. 57. p. 337.
[3] *Diary of Thomas Burton.* ed. T. Birch. i. 259. 1828.

which had gone before in Hatfield Chase and the Great Level, but with a different outcome. Discounting any influence which might have been exercised on the Commons by the petition of Thornton and King, it would appear that the more democratic outlook and constitution of Parliament in the years of the Protectorate created more consideration for the rights of the commoners than had existed in the monarchial times of Charles, and that in spite of the friendship, or, at least, the close relationship, between Cromwell and Vermuyden, this was not allowed to interfere with what was considered to be the just rights of individuals, however humble.

And that was the end of Sir Cornelius Vermuyden's attempts to drain Sedgmoor. It was, indeed, the historical end of Vermuyden himself because with that entry in Thomas Burton's Diary, and with an entry to the same effect in the Commons' Journal, he faded away from the pages of history. Sedgmoor remained undrained for many more years. Indeed, it was not enclosed and allotted until after the passing of the King's Sedgmoor Enclosure Act of 1791. Vermuyden may have made some later attempts to have the decision of December 1656 revised, but there is nothing on the record to show this. It is difficult to think that a man of his determination would have let the matter rest there. Assuming that the date of his birth in 1590 is correct, in the year 1656 he was only sixty-six years of age and far from being too old to retain his energy for the project. The 4,000 acres of Sedgmoor may have been of little value in their 'drowned' state and yet these lands represented one of his possessions with which he refused to part. It is not true to say that Vermuyden sold his lands in Sedgmoor. He did not, and, as will be shown later, these descended to his son Cornelius and were the subject of much dispute in later years. The failure of the bill to pass in 1656 must have been a disappointment to him and possibly he may have made further attempts to gain his objective, but certainly without success. It must not be overlooked that four years later came the Restoration and it is conceivable that the close and confidential relationship which had existed between Sir Cornelius and Oliver Cromwell may have made the former far from *persona grata* in the court of Charles II, in spite of the earlier intimate connection with the restored King's father and grandfather. Indeed, that may explain to some extent the continuance in obscurity of the Vermuyden family after the Restoration. An interesting sidelight on this aspect is provided by the Rev. Abraham de la Pryme, of whom mention has been made earlier, in a letter which he wrote on 9th March, 1702/3, to a Mr. Parrol [*sic*] in London. In this letter he refers to his History of Hatfield Chase which he had then 'almost finished in some hundreds of sheets of paper' and then goes on to ask Parolle—a descendant of David Parolle who had been a

Surveyor in Hatfield Chase—whether he can supply him with any information concerning the Vermuydens, the Vernattis and others, and particularly wants to know what became of 'Sir Cornelius Vermeuden's [*sic*] son and two daughters, or where they live, that I might write or go to them'.[1] De la Pryme was, of course, a long way out in his reckoning in referring to the 'son and two daughters' because Sir Cornelius's family extended much beyond these limits, but the letter does indicate that even in 1702 there was a certain elusiveness about the Vermuyden family, and their story, particularly after the end of Sir Cornelius's connection with the Great Level, becomes largely one of assumption and presumption. This might be considered a somewhat strange state of affairs if account is taken of the undoubtedly important position which he had occupied during a period of some thirty-five years.

[1] *The Diary of Abraham de la Pryme*, edited by Charles Jackson, the Surtees Society, 1870.

CHAPTER FIFTEEN

Evaluation of Vermuyden's principles, and of his work in the Great Level, primarily on the basis of the 'Discourse'.

AND so ends in speculation the story of Cornelius Vermuyden and the Great Level of the Fens. All that is left to do is to sum up with the added experience of nearly three hundred years in an attempt to assess the quality of his achievement. Let it first be realised that in making a critical evaluation of Vermuyden's work in the Great Level there is the danger of allowing the difficulties and hazards with which he had to contend to influence the technical criticism. There is no denying these difficulties and hazards, but while their overcoming adds lustre to the achievement it does not in any way affect the judgement of the rightness or wrongness of the principles of drainage which he adopted. The lack of accurate maps, the primitive nature of survey methods and instruments, the lack of precedent, the opposition of vested interests, the shortage of money, all added their burden to the task, but they in no way modified the methods and principles which Vermuyden adopted and on which his reputation as a drainage engineer must stand or fall. On the other hand, while it might appear at first sight to be unfair to judge his achievement on the basis of present-day hydraulic knowledge, yet the only practical standard of comparison which can be employed is the relation which the scheme he evolved and carried out in the seventeenth century bears to what would be done now, assuming a beginning *de novo* with conditions in the Great Level, as they were in the first half of that century. This, at least, does give a standard of comparison which is more than most of the contemporary critics deigned to employ, preferring, mainly, to indulge in vindictive cavilling and later to repeat and embellish earlier criticisms as an extension of the game of discrediting Vermuyden and his accomplishments.

The obvious starting-point in any examination of Vermuyden's work is the *Discourse touching the draining of the Great Fennes* of 1642. This, as has been said earlier, is the only record which we have, in Vermuyden's own words, of the principles of drainage which he had evolved at this period and of the methods by which he intended to drain the Great Level. While in actuality there were certain departures from, and modifications to, the 'Discourse' in the methods eventually employed, the principles remained unaltered.

When King James had declared himself undertaker for the draining of the Level in 1621, Vermuyden was, as he tells us, 'come over to England invited to this work'. In his own words 'I took several views thereof, went away, returned, and reviewed the same, took advice of the experienced men of the Low Countries, and from time to time did study how to contrive that work for the best advantage'. In the year 1621 any experience which Vermuyden possessed was only that which he had gained in Holland. To take 'advice of the experienced men of the Low Countries' seems to have been a sensible course, but this does not necessarily mean that, seventeen years later when the 'Discourse' was written, this advice was then indiscriminately acted upon. In the intervening period there had come the mistakes made and the consequent experience gained in Hatfield Chase and by 1642 it is quite evident that Vermuyden was fully alive to the fact that the general drainage principles employed in Holland were not necessarily the right solution for the Great Level.

Jan Barents Westerdyke, Vermuyden's rival for the work of draining the Great Level, enunciated very different principles and, as is the way with rivals, was very condemnatory of Vermuyden's principles and if, as Skertchley said in the nineteenth century, it is true that Westerdyke was 'among the first to show that the conditions of the English and Dutch fens are totally different'[1] this does not destroy the fact that Vermuyden also was quite aware of this difference and said so in the 'Discourse'. Indeed he would have been a fool if he had failed to see the difference and to plan accordingly. And Sir Cornelius was no fool.

Fundamentally Westerdyke maintained that the correct course to pursue was to retain the natural system of drainage by embanking and cleaning out existing rivers as opposed to Vermuyden's proposal to replace existing winding rivers by straight new cuts such as the Old and New Bedford Rivers. Vermuyden pointed out that 'there is in use a general rule of Drayning and gaining of drowned lands, which is by embanking all the rivers on each side . . . but in thee case of the Great Fenns, I cannot advise to go altogether in such a way' because, as he said, by this plan 'a multitude of banks must be made, about 70,000 rods in length, on a level and moorish ground'. He realised that the construction of such banks out of the peaty soil would be both structurally unsatisfactory and economically unsound from the point of view of maintenance costs.

[1] S. B. J. Skertchley. *The Geology of the Fenland.* 1877.

Unfortunately Skertchley, however admirable may have been his conclusions on the geology of the Fenland, committed the common fault of adopting the criticisms of Vermuyden advanced by his predecessors, notably Samuel Wells, without troubling to make an independent judgement of his own. In commenting upon the difference between the low lands of Holland and England he points out that 'the former lay below the ordinary level of the sea, and had no natural drainage, the latter lay entirely above mean tide level and possessed an adequate drainage system of its own'. But that is exactly what it did not possess, as otherwise no improvement in the system would have been necessary, and while the statement that the Great Level lay above mean tide level may have been true at the time Vermuyden was devising his scheme, it was certainly not true some years after that scheme had been completed. The state of affairs which prevailed then, brought about by the shrinkage of the peat and silt areas, was largely responsible for the defective draining of parts of the Great Level in spite of Vermuyden's work, and it is not suggested that he achieved one hundred per cent. success, but Vermuyden is less blameworthy for not anticipating something of which neither he, nor anybody else at the time, knew anything than is Skertchley for failing to recognise something which was there before his eyes.

Skertchley suggests that, as a positive remedy, 'what should have been done, and what I think all modern engineers and most of those of the past agree upon, was to have directed the chief attention to the improvement and maintenance of existing outfalls'. That the state of the outfalls of the Fenland rivers into the Wash was a dominating factor in the drainage of the Fens cannot be denied. The two main rivers contributing to the drainage of the Great Level, the Nene and the Ouse, bring practically no silt with them in their courses from the uplands to the sea. Silting up of their mouths in the Wash, however, is caused if the quantities of silt brought in from the Wash itself to the lower tidal reaches on the flood tide are inadequately scoured out on the succeeding ebb tide, and by the fresh water flowing through the outfall from the upper reaches. The widespread effect of a choked or partially choked outfall is exemplified by the abandonment of the Wisbech outfall by the River Ouse and the diversion to King's Lynn which, as has been described earlier, occurred many centuries before Vermuyden's day.

In our brief examination of the 'Discourse' in Chapter IX we have already pointed out that Vermuyden, far from neglecting or ignoring the question of the outfalls, put forward the definite proposal for uniting the Welland and the Nene in order that 'they may (in time) gain themselves a natural channel, which will be far better than to leave them to sundry outfalls'. This was his remedy for the choking every summer of the outfalls of these two rivers when the discharge from the rivers was at a minimum. As far as the King's Lynn outfall of the Ouse was concerned he considered that that outfall 'hath sufficient water to keep open his channel'. That, perhaps, may have been a somewhat optimistic forecast, but, nevertheless, there is ample evidence to show that Vermuyden did anything but neglect to consider the outfalls. What he was permitted to do by his employers, the Earl of Bedford and his fellow Adventurers, is another matter for which he cannot be expected to bear the blame.

It will be recalled that Vermuyden in commenting on Sir Clement Edmonds' report of 1618 had pointed out that that report had emphasised that 'it was likewise found good to draw the waters to their ancient outfalls' and as both the Welland and the Nene had anciently had a common outfall at Wisbech, his proposal was made with that end in view. Of course, it might be argued that the logical development of this would have been to restore the Ouse to the outfall at Wisbech, but a little consideration will show that such a violent and drastic upheaval of what had become the natural drainage system would have been entirely out of the question.

There is not the slightest doubt that Vermuyden fully appreciated the bearing of the outfalls on his, or anybody else's, system of drainage of the Great Level. His proposed plan of uniting the Welland and the Nene was not only sound, but well in advance of his time. This, perhaps, was the reason why he was not permitted to put it into effect, but just over one hundred years later, in 1751, Nathaniel Kinderley, who gained a sound reputation in the matter of the drainage of the Fens, proposed a scheme on similar lines except that he intended to unite the Nene with the Ouse and the Welland with the Witham. After the passage of almost another hundred years, in 1839, Sir John Rennie, whose reputation needs no emphasis, was advising the much more ambitious scheme of uniting all four rivers, Ouse, Welland, Nene and Witham, into one grand combined outfall into the Wash. The fact that neither of these two later proposals was adopted does not in any way detract from the merit of Vermuyden's prophetical vision in seeing the problem from the same angle as his more enlightened, and more respected, successors.

Throughout the whole of the 'Discourse' it is possible to see that Vermuyden had made a very close study and sound appreciation of the conditions with which he had to contend in the Great Level, and there is not the slightest indication that he had slavishly adhered to principles which had been adopted in Holland, or that he had blindly followed 'the advice of the experienced men of the Low Countries', which, quite rightly, he had taken

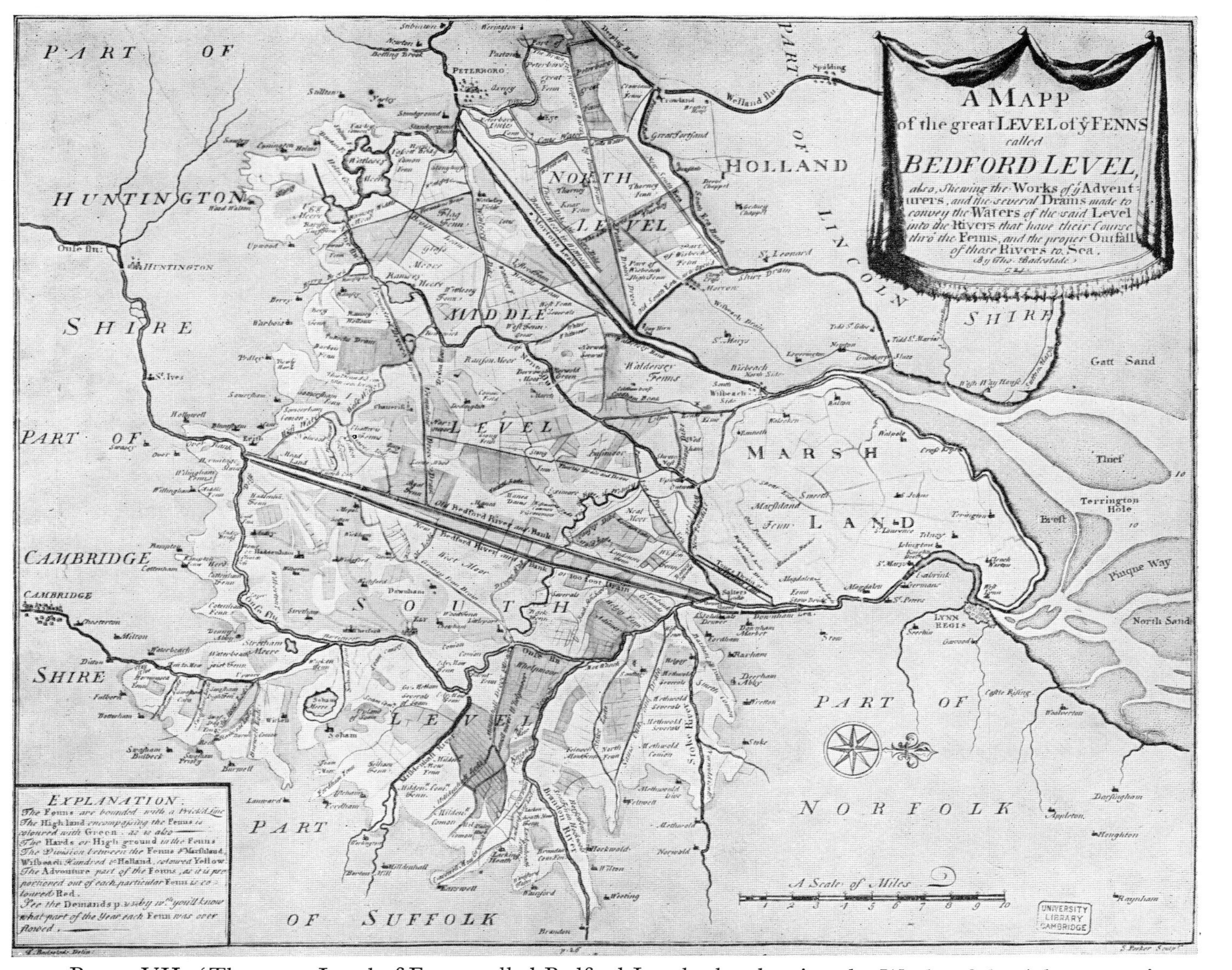

PLATE VII. 'The great Level of Fenns called Bedford Level, also showing the Works of the Adventurers'.

from T. Badeslade: *History of the Navigation of King's Lynn*, 1725.

in 1621. But one important fact must not be overlooked. When the 'Discourse' was written in 1638 and published in 1642 there were already in existence in the Great Level the works of drainage which Vermuyden had carried out from 1631 to 1638 for the first undertaking of Francis, Earl of Bedford, under the Lynn Law. As future history was to show, Vermuyden suffered severely from lack of freedom to execute all the works which he advised and as, unfortunately, no written record of his recommendations for this first undertaking have so far come to light, it is impossible to say whether he was permitted then to carry out this scheme as he had designed it. In any case, the result was not satisfactory financially to the Earl of Bedford and whether technically the scheme did achieve just 'the summer grounds' which, Vermuyden maintained, were all that were called for, it is difficult to say. The adverse judgement of the Huntingdon Commission of 1638 may have been due to defects in Vermuyden's original scheme. By 1642 he had to think again, perhaps with the knowledge of partial failure behind him, and certainly with the nucleus of a scheme already imposed on the Great Level, a nucleus which could not be simply expunged, but on which he had to build again to achieve the wider result of 'winter grounds'. The work which he had completed by 1638 was not, in truth, of very wide extent if we compare it with what was done in later years and what, indeed, exists today. But by 1638 Vermuyden was fundamentally committed to the scheme which he laid down in the 'Discourse' because he had already constructed the 21-mile-long staight cut, the Bedford River, which augmented and, to a large extent replaced, the tortuous 30-mile course of the River Ouse between Earith and Denver.

Departing for the moment from the consideration of the work, as such, involved in the 'Discourse', it is necessary to comment on the division of the Level which Vermuyden laid down therein. His conclusion was that it was 'the fittest way to divide the whole level into three parts.

1. The one from Glean [Glen] to Morton's Leam.
2. From Morton's Leam to Bedford River.
3. From Bedford River southwards, being the remainder of the Level.'

These divisions subsequently became known as the North, Middle and South Levels respectively.

Now if there was one thing of which Vermuyden was fully aware it was that in order to drain the Great Level effectively it was absolutely necessary to adopt an all-embracing, comprehensive scheme. In other words, he was convinced that all parts of the Level were interdependent, a conviction which was reinforced by knowledge of the disastrous failures of piecemeal attempts in the past. To say that 'he put asunder that which Nature had joined, and divided the Bedford Level into three portions—North, Middle and South, whose common interests were then made to clash to a degree which none but the hereditary occupiers can adequately estimate'[1] was merely a Victorian expression in extravagant terms of a complete inability to understand what Vermuyden was aiming at. If there was to be any plan in the drainage scheme it was necessary to decide through what channels and to what outfalls the various parts of the level were to drain and Miller and Skertchley's statement could be construed into a belief that the whole of the Great Level should have been drained into one main river. Which was absurd. If in later years the administrative and financial barriers between the three levels did lead to some lack of co-ordination, that was no fault of Vermuyden's.

The purpose of discussing here this question of the division of the Great Level into three parts has not been solely to discredit Miller and Skertchley. Whatever criticisms have been made of Vermuyden's work in the past three hundred years there is no denying that in the main such criticisms have been advanced against the work in the South Level where, there is little doubt, the greatest difficulties have been encountered, and are being encountered to-day. That circumstance was not the result of Vermuyden's division of the Great Level into three. Natural conditions were to make it inevitable, a fact recognised by Vermuyden when he said 'that this part of the country is more overflown and dangerously drowned than any other parts of the fenn are'. But, and this is the important point, it would appear as if the work which Vermuyden did in, or for the drainage of, the South Level between the years 1650 and 1653 was, to a great extent, forced upon him by the conditions which he had himself created by his earlier undertaking under the Lynn Law. The Old Bedford River was there. The principle which it represented called for the New Bedford, or Hundred Foot, River, which in turn created the Washlands between the two, and eventually compelled the construction of Denver Sluice. After the adjudication of 1653 the North and Middle Levels settled down to a comparatively uneventful existence and one relatively free from flooding. But it was not long before it became unpleasantly apparent that things were far from well in the South Level. Flooding became commonplace and long after Vermuyden had disappeared controversies raged round the two Bedford Rivers, the Washlands, and Denver Sluice. Was he to blame for this state of affairs by what he did, or was he the victim of what he was not allowed to do?

[1] S. H. Miller and S. B. Skertchley, *The Fenland Past and Present.* 1878.

CHAPTER SIXTEEN

The principle of the Bedford Rivers and of washes. The proposed cut-off channel. Denver Sluice and its repercussions. Rennie's scheme of 1810. Flood Prevention scheme of 1953 compared with Vermuyden's.

To answer these questions it is first necessary to try and understand the subsidiary aim, or aims, which Vermuyden had in view. Quite obviously one of his main objects was to avoid, as he said, 'multiplicity of banks, which are very chargeable both in their making and maintaining' and, dealing with the South Level only, the original purpose of the Bedford River was to relieve the winding Ouse of part of the upland water by turning these into the Bedford River at Earith. Thus it was anticipated that the level in the Ouse would be lowered and the necessity of high and costly banks of 'moorish soil' avoided. But it must not be overlooked that the Bedford River was not an original conception of Vermuyden's. In June 1605 a 'view of the whole level' was undertaken by a commission of sewers headed by Sir Robert Bevill, and in its report the commission clearly stated that 'the making of a new river from Erith Bridge through Sutton, Beryall and Westmore Fens, to Wellenhey River, and thence through certain Fens of Norfolk into the Ouse about Mayd lode, would be most necessary; and that without so doing the Fens could never be drained.'[1]

By the time the 'Discourse' came to be written in 1642 Vermuyden realised that the remedy of the Bedford River was not in itself enough to protect the South Level since between Earith and Denver the Ouse received the waters of the Cam, the Lark, the Little Ouse and the Wissey draining from the uplands of Suffolk and Norfolk. Therefore, with this realisation, and to protect the Middle Level and the South Level, he planned to unite the Lark, the Little Ouse, and the Wissey in one common channel and to discharge them into the Ouse below the junction of that river with the Bedford River. That was what he planned. What in fact he did was to cut the Hundred Foot River parallel with and to the east of the Bedford

[1] DUGDALE. *Op. cit.*, p. 381.

River, the inner bank of each being made comparatively low so that the flood waters of both at low levels would spill over into the Washlands between them, to be stored there until the outfall at King's Lynn was capable of dealing with this excess flow.

The principle of washes was not, as we have shown much earlier, any new departure for Vermuyden, but it was something entirely opposed to any principles held by Westerdyke. According to Elstobb,[1] when Westerdyke was called in by William, Earl of Bedford to comment on and criticise Vermuyden's scheme in 1650, he reported that 'in respect to setting of banks at such distances as Sir Cornelius directed, in some places near a mile asunder . . . Sir Cornelius could give him no reason'. That, of course, is palpably an absurdity as Vermuyden had stated that 'I resolve to imitate nature (as much as can be) in the Upland Countries for between the hills are meadows, and on each side pasture grounds or plough land, I shall endeavour to contrive the workes that way, that there be meadows between the uplands and the winter ground of the fenns likewise', and again, 'For that the meadows will be receptacles for the water in time of extremity to bed on upon all occasions of floods, and so to keep the waters at a lesser height by far against the banks.'

Thus he clearly enunciated his principle of washes and more explicitly on the subject of banks, laid down that 'the banks . . . must be a great distance the one from the other, so that the water, in time of extremity, may go in a large room to keep it from rising too high'. Nothing could be simpler than that.

To relieve the Ouse above Denver of the upland water of Norfolk and Suffolk, Vermuyden planned to unite the Lark, the Little Ouse and the Wissey into a cut-off channel running roughly parallel to the Ouse which would eventually discharge these waters into the Ouse below Denver where, as he said, 'the fall is good and sufficient'. This intention is clearly shown on the map which accompanied the 'Discourse', but unfortunately and for reasons unknown, the intention was never put into effect. This may have been due to financial stringency and hence 'comptrollment' on the part of the Adventurers, but, whatever the reason, there is no doubt that omission of the cut-off channel was a factor greatly contributing to the comparative failure of Vermuyden's scheme in the South Level. The channel does not appear to have formed part of his original scheme and, like the Hundred Foot and the Washlands between it and the Old Bedford River, was probably an afterthought which experience had shown to be necessary, certainly for the creation of winter grounds. After all, in the absence of any well

[1] W. Elstobb, *Observations on an Address to the Public*, 1776.

developed hydraulic science, Vermuyden and all his contemporaries were dependent upon intelligent anticipation. The wonder is not that he was so often right but that he was so seldom wrong.

And so we come to Denver Sluice on the Ouse at the junction with the Hundred Foot just above Downham and one of the most controversial features of the whole of Vermuyden's work. A book could be written about Denver Sluice and, indeed, one has been written,[1] but during the whole of the three hundred years which have elapsed since the first sluice was built in 1651 there never has been any unanimity of opinion on the need for its existence. Indeed, this lack of unanimity has not been confined to the subject of the Denver Sluice. As we know there was a distinct divergence of opinion in the early seventeenth century as to the best methods to be employed in the Fens in general. At one time a cause of divergence was the necessarily antagonistic attitude of the drainage and the navigational interests, but even now when to a large extent the latter have disappeared there is still a conflict of opinion on methods for a particular purpose. The conclusion to be drawn from this is that the drainage of the Fens was in Vermuyden's time, and, to a lesser extent, still is a problem indeterminable by any hard and fast rule. But, nevertheless, it requires something akin to genius to find the best solution.

On 14th June, 1649, Colonel Dodson had, as we know, 'declared his Designe for the setting of a Sluice on the River Ouse', and from this we can conclude that Vermuyden's original scheme, which existed then on the Great Level, and which included the Old Bedford River, had provided for no such Sluice. If Vermuyden never had any intention of putting a sluice at Denver, and there is no indication that he had, then by present day judgement his scheme in the South Level was incomplete. Today Denver Sluice exercises two functions. It prevents the silt-laden tidal water from flowing up the Ouse (this is diverted up the Hundred Foot) and thus prevents silting up of the Ouse itself, and, by the same token, it obviates the need for the banks of the Ouse above Denver to be high enough to withstand the high tidal levels. It is wrong, however, to ascribe these benefits to Vermuyden. The credit must go to Colonel Dodson. Or as the pamphleteers of the eighteenth and nineteenth centuries would have said, the discredit.

It is not entirely true to say that the drainage and navigational interests were completely divergent as both had certain common aims, but in criticising Denver Sluice it is necessary to ensure that there is a clear understanding of the interest which is involved. A study of Thomas Badeslade's book *The History of the . . . Navigation of the Port of King's Lynn*, and of the

[1] T. BADESLADE, *The History of the . . . Navigation of the Port of King's Lynn*. 1725.

objections adduced against Denver Sluice, which form the bulk of the book, make it quite clear that the arguments bear out the implication of the title, viz., that Badeslade is concerned solely with the navigational interests. Generally speaking, therefore, his criticisms as a commentary on the work of Vermuyden are practically useless, a point of view which was often overlooked by the non-technical section of Vermuyden's detractors. A much more valuable critic was John Smeaton who, in his report of 1767, even though he was speaking from the point of view of the Harbour of King's Lynn, said 'Denver Sluice is much too far up from the outfall to work any considerable effect either way; but that the natural effect of it as well as the 100-foot drain, so far as they operate on the Harbour of Lynn and sea channel below, must be rather beneficial'. Then again John Golborne who, while he never gained the fame of Smeaton was a recognised authority on the drainage of the Fens, wrote in 1777 that 'The altering of the course of this river, [i.e. the cutting of the Hundred Foot] and turning it down a new channel, in a somewhat higher situation, has been censured by many; yet I must vindicate the idea, as founded on sound principles, and according to the established rules of draining; though I must censure the mode in which it was executed, as being productive of many of the misfortunes under which the level now labours.'

On the subject of the Hundred Foot River, Sir John Rennie reported in 1839 that 'The shortening of the course of the Ouse was beneficial, as far as regarded the Middle Level, by giving an increased fall to the current, and thereby getting rid of the floods from the interior, but was injurious to the South Level, by checking the discharge of the upland and downfall waters from the district . . . but had a different course been adopted, the Hundred Foot River would not have been prejudicial either to the South Level or to the Lynn Outfall.'

Now those are the opinions of three engineers of experience and established reputation and from these it will be seen that while Smeaton attributes no adverse effect on the Port of King's Lynn to either Denver Sluice or the Hundred Foot River, both Golborne and Rennie approved of the Hundred Foot in principle, but disapproved, presumably, of the nature of work done on the River Ouse itself and on Denver Sluice.

Denver Sluice was constructed first in 1651, but the details of this design are not known. It was reconstructed in 1682 to the designs of Sir Thomas Fitch and in 1713, owing to undermining of the foundations, 'blew up' and was completely destroyed. Charles Labelye, the designer of the first Westminster Bridge over the Thames, was called in to advise on the drainage of the Great Level in 1745 and eventually in 1751 rebuilt Denver Sluice when, after years of bitter argument, the opinion that the sluice was necessary for the drainage of the South Level prevailed. The condition in the Level after the sluice had blown up in 1713 proved this, but the antagonists of the sluice admitted that the necessity was forced upon the drainage only by reason of the existence of the Hundred Foot which, they maintained, was a mistake and a failure in the first place. Labelye's comments on the Denver Sluice as constructed in 1682 are illuminating. 'First the breadth of the River Old Ouse (which just about Denver was then above 150 feet wide, and has to this day 124 Feet free water way through Downham Bridge, which is but a little lower) was reduced by Abutments of Brick, faced with stone, to barely 80 feet. Across this pitiful outfall for so many rivers, the people who executed it were supposed to build a solid wall or dam eight feet perpendicular above the bottom of the Old Ouse . . . Over the close Dam were erected a Bridge and other Works that left only three openings of 18 feet wide each . . . to compleat the matter, three pair of Breast Gates, pointing to seaward, were placed over this Dam . . . Lastly, so little regard was had to the inland Navigation, that no lock was provided . . . Whoever was Director of this Work, whether Sir Cornelius himself, or as I have been told, Sir John Fitch, of the Borough of Southwark, (a Man famous even to this day among the Boys for his celebrated Fleet Ditch) must be taxed with an Ignorance which is almost criminal.'[1]

A copy of the contract for the construction of the sluice dated 20th December, 1682 between 'the right honourable the Governor, Bayliffs and Comonalty of the Company of Conservators of the Great Levell of the Fenns called Bedford Levell on the one part and John Hayward of the parish of St. Saviours, Southwark in the County of Surrey Carpenter of the other part' has recently come to light[2] wherein is specified the manner in which the sluice is to be built 'according to the Platt or Draft hereunto annexed or otherwise as Sir Thomas Fitch knight shall direct'. Whether during the course of construction alterations were made in the dimensions as laid down in the agreement is not clear, but this agreement stipulates that the three openings were to have 'Twenty Foot cleare water way in breadth', although on the drawings this measurement scales only seventeen feet six inches. But whatever the dimensions, and even admitting that the total width of waterway was not sufficient as suggested by Labelye, it was not Sir Cornelius Vermuyden who could, in this instance, 'be taxed with an Ignorance which is almost criminal'. By the year 1682 he had long disappeared from the Great Level. Sir Thomas Fitch (not John as Labelye says) and the then

[1] *The Result of a View of the Great Level of the Fens*, 1745.
[2] Middle Level Commissioners' Documents.

Director of Works must share the blame. Vermuyden is usually, and rightly, given the credit for the making of the Old Bedford and the Hundred Foot Rivers, but it is clear that the conception of these was not his. When he first made the Old Bedford River in 1632 he was only carrying out something the necessity for which had been advocated in 1605 and when in later years the apparent inadequacy of this river was appreciated he then cut the Hundred Foot to make up the deficiency. It might appear that he was at fault in not realising that Denver Sluice was a necessary corollary to the Hundred Foot, and even, indeed, to the Old Bedford River, but while this is to a certain extent true it must not be overlooked that the scheme that he had laid down in the 'Discourse' had intended the employment of means for the protection of the South Level which was, after all, the primary function of Denver Sluice. Referring to Sir John Rennie's report of 1839 quoted above, the 'shortening of the course of the Ouse' would not have been 'injurious to the South Level' if the scheme proposed by Vermuyden had been accepted whereby the rivers Lark, Little Ouse and Wissey had been united into one cut-off channel and then discharged into the River Ouse *below* Denver Sluice and after that river had, in fact, left the South Level altogether. By this means the quantity of water with which the Ouse would have had to deal *above* Denver Sluice would have been very substantially reduced and, in spite of the sluice being sometimes kept closed for long periods owing to the higher level of the waters in the Hundred Foot the Ouse itself would probably have been able to deal with the storage of this reduced quantity without flooding into the South Level. As far as the dimensions of Denver Sluice are concerned, even if as originally constructed these were inadequate it must be remembered that Vermuyden no doubt designed these to deal with the reduced discharge of the Ouse which would result from the employment of his cut-off channel. What Sir Thomas Fitch did in 1682 could be no concern of Sir Cornelius.

The troubles experienced in the South Level after the completion of Vermuyden's scheme in 1653 were not due primarily to either the Hundred Foot River or to Denver Sluice. The main causes were, firstly that the scheme was, in fact, never completed in that his cut-off channel common to the Rivers Lark, Little Ouse and Wissey was never constructed, and, secondly, that while the channel of the Ouse was restricted by the inadequate capacity of Denver Sluice, lower down it was further restricted by the existence of tortuous bends below Denver. Or as Golborne said, 'The evil lay in the wide and shallow channel between Germans and Lynn: for it had the same effect as a dam of 4 feet 9 inches, made over the river to pen it up'. When Golborne was writing, about one hundred and twenty years after the end of Vermuyden's work, the South Level was in a parlous condition for, as he said, 'look which way you will, you see nothing but misery and desolation; go but half a mile from Ely, and you come to Middle Fen, a tract of 16,000 acres given up and abandoned; there you see the ruin of windmills, the last efforts of an industrious people. If to Ramsey, there you find more than 10,000 acres occupied by the waters, and see houses without inhabitants, and lands incapable of either pasturage or tillage'.

From Golborne's own words it is evident that the land in question had at one time had a settled cultivation as is evidenced by the existence both of ruined windmills and of deserted houses.

All this misery and desolation could not be laid at the door of Sir Cornelius Vermuyden. It was in fact, and indeed very largely, due to the lowering of the surface of the peat land, the result as we know now of the action of aerobic bacteria on the dry peat resulting from the drainage itself. Colonel Dodson was, perhaps, the first to draw attention to the shrinkage of the peat in his 'Discourse' of 1664 although from what he said then it is apparent that he had no idea of the true significance of this happening, nor of the extent to which it would develop. As for 'the wide and shallow channel between Germans and Lynn' Golborne was not the first to point this out. Nathaniel Kinderley for instance, in 1751 advocated the cutting of a new channel for the Ouse 'in a strait line from half a mile below Germans, (viz., at a place called Eau-Brink) to half a mile above Lyn, which would be a course of but two Miles in length; and so to desert the present broad, unconfined, shallow and crooked course (which the River now takes) of between 6 and 7 miles in Length'.[1] But seventy more years were to pass before, in 1821, the Eau Brink cut was made as an essential part of the scheme which John Rennie carried out on the basis of his report of 1810.[2] This will give some idea of the indecision, the procrastination with which all advocates of remedial measures in the Fens have been faced. And none more so than Vermuyden who was working at a time when there was even less enlightenment than existed in the succeeding centuries.

In the early years after the completion of Vermuyden's work in the Great Level when, in particular, conditions in the South Level were undoubtedly bad, there were many who were prepared to criticise that work adversely. In a long list of critics we find Westerdyke, Edmund Scotton, Richard Lord Gorges, Col. Armstrong, Badeslade, all with some pretension to professional knowledge, and many others, but as time went on the adverse criticism was generally left to the unprofessional writers such as

[1] N. Kinderley, *The Ancient and Present State of the Navigation of the Towne of Lyn, etc.* 1751.

[2] *Report and Estimate on the Improvement of the Drainage and Navigation of the South and Middle Levels.* 1810.

Wells, Miller and Skertchley who based their views more on the expressed opinions of others than on their own knowledge and reasoning. Not that professional adverse criticism disappeared completely. As late as 1846 Lewis Gordon, a civil engineer, a Fellow of the Royal Society, in a report on the work to be carried out under the Norfolk Estuary Act wrote the following.

'The measures taken from time to time for shortening the course of the rivers, so as to increase their scour and thus lower the low water mark, or for confining and regulating the stream in its natural channel, evince perception of the true maxims of drainage on the one hand and of ill adapted temporary expedient on the other. The application of the Dutch practice, as unfortunately introduced into this country by Sir Cornelius Vermuyden, to a case beyond its range, and with a judgment biased by selfish considerations, long delayed and still seems to obstruct the recognition of the laws of hydraulics suited to the particular circumstances of this estuary.'

Gordon was, of course, fully entitled to his opinion but, in our view he laboured under two disadvantages. Firstly, he started from the erroneous premise that Vermuyden unjustifiably introduced the 'Dutch practice' into the Great Level, and secondly, he spoils any technical criticisms by the interpolation of a personal vindictiveness in the accusation of 'selfish considerations'. This latter fault, however understandable in Andrewes Burrell and his contemporaries of the seventeenth century, has gradually been eliminated from more modern professional, and therefore qualified, criticism.

It has been said earlier that the only practical standard of comparison to apply to Vermuyden's work is how the drainage of the Great Level would be carried out today, assuming that conditions in, and the state of, the Level were as they existed in the mid-seventeenth century. Would a similar plan be adopted? Would the twin Bedford Rivers be cut with the washlands in between? Would Denver Sluice be built? Very difficult questions to answer and the fact that the new Flood Relief Scheme to be carried out in the South Level by the Great Ouse River Board embodies a cut-off channel for the Lark, the Little Ouse and the Wissey, almost identical to that advocated by Vermuyden, and a relief channel below Denver as he also advocated, does not necessarily mean that present-day knowledge endorses his judgement. It might be argued that these two features are merely compulsory expedients forced on the modern drainage engineer by the fact that Vermuyden's scheme exists and must be made to work, in spite of the Bedford Rivers, the Washlands and Denver Sluice. That might be the conclusion, but even if it were then it would still constitute undeniable proof that, if

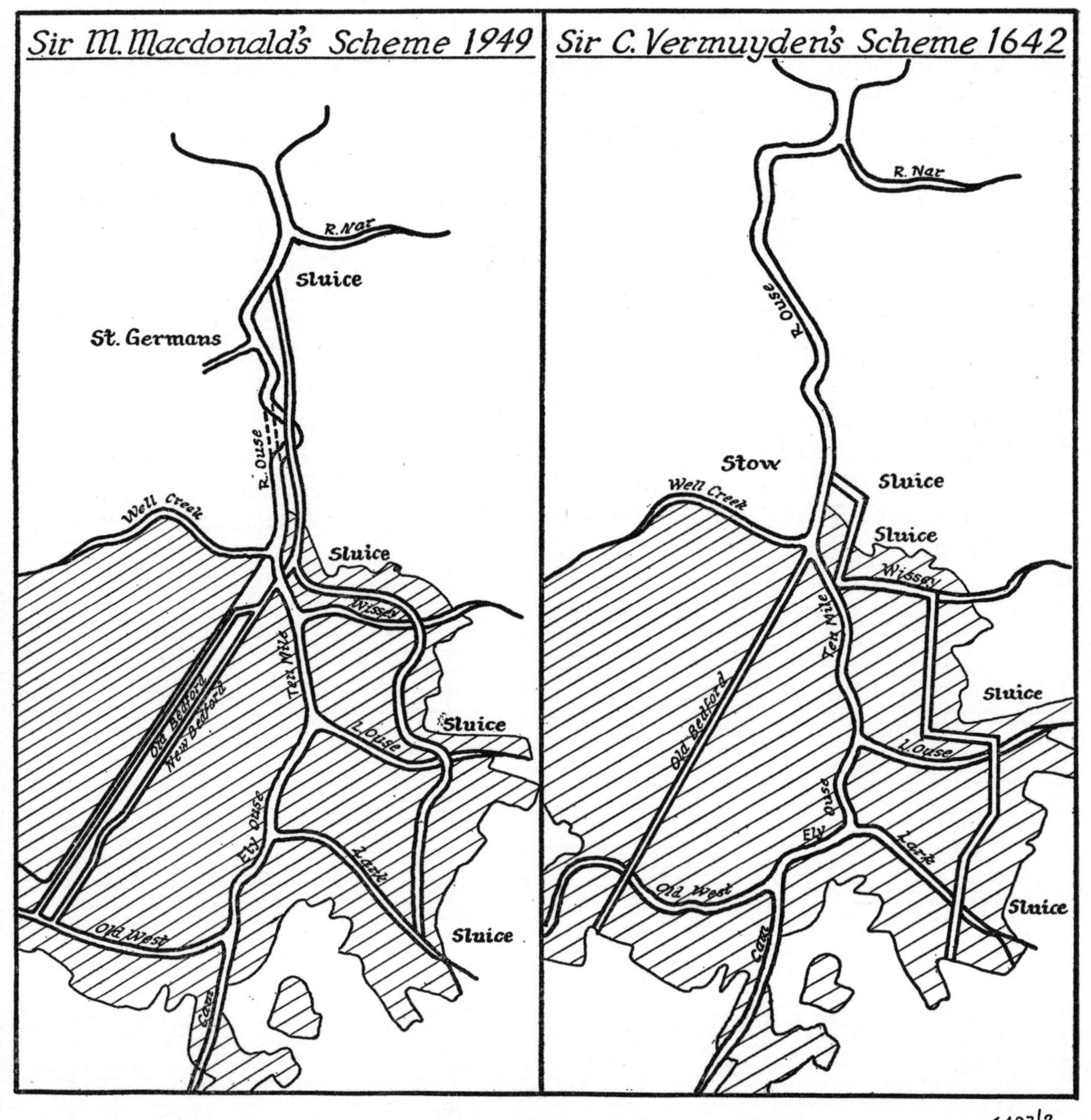

Comparison of Vermuyden's scheme of 1642 with projected modern flood relief scheme.

Vermuyden had been allowed to make his cut-off channel and his relief channel, both of which he clearly laid down in the 'Discourse', then his scheme would have proved even more successful than in fact it did; and certainly as successful as modern knowledge, three hundred years after his time, can make it today. Furthermore, as time has gone on and as hydraulic knowledge, knowledge of the behaviour of rivers, and, in particular, knowledge of the Fenland rivers and of the Fens themselves have increased through systematised observation, so has the professional verdict on Vermuyden's work become more favourable. An indication that Vermuyden was subconsciously thinking in terms of hydraulic development which was still three centuries ahead.

The twin Bedford Rivers which run in almost parallel straight lines for twenty-one miles across the flat expanse of the Bedford Level may not be the original conception of Vermuyden, but he made them and they epitomise the thought and labour which over a period of more than thirty years he gave to the Level. And thus they constitute a visible memorial to a man to whom posterity can, however belatedly, with justice offer some tribute of respect.

CHAPTER SEVENTEEN

Vermuyden's character. His career after departure from Great Level. His children. The Wirksworth Lead Mine.

THE story of Sir Cornelius Vermuyden and the Great Level of the Fens ended on 4th February, 1655, with the entry in the Proceedings of his final attendance at a meeting of the Company of Adventurers. The further story of Vermuyden himself continues until his death in 1677. The tale which has been related so far has of necessity, and to a certain extent intentionally, been somewhat impersonal, the object having been to examine and assess the value of the work in the Great Level rather than the man himself. In the relation of this tale momentary revelations of personality and character have occurred and, it must be admitted, the resulting illumination has not shed an entirely favourable light on Sir Cornelius. The episode of Dagenham, the isolated incident quoted of the Wirksworth affair, the implications of the Hatfield undertaking, the accusation concerning the purchase of Sedgmoor, could all be interpreted as evidence of an unsavoury personality, particularly by those seeking for unfavourable signs to confirm a preconceived opinion.

The technical achievements of Vermuyden in his works of land reclamation form the basis on which his success or failure must be judged in relation to the Great Level, and that has been the purpose of this book. Nor is it felt that there is any valid reason why the judgement of success should be withheld from him. But there is another side to the story, the private life of Sir Cornelius Vermuyden, and this is a story more difficult to piece together. Whatever may have been the cause of his final breach with, or parting from, the Bedford Level Adventurers, there is no denying that he was a successful man in many ways, and a man who achieved much through his own energy. All his manifold activities involved him in difficult and complicated transactions, both financial and commercial, and it must be remembered that success such as he achieved was bound to bring jealousy in its train. The many suits in the Chancery Court in which Vermuyden was involved, either as defendant or plaintiff, show that not only was he himself a litigious man, but that, also, it was a litigious age in which he lived. He was a hard man of business and one of his rewards was the accusations of his rivals, some of which, we must admit, may have been true. Doubtless also a great deal of contemporary prejudice was due to Vermuyden's dominating and aggressive nature, more suited to the gaining of his own objectives than to the making of friends.

One point however, must not be overlooked. It was one of Vermuyden's misfortunes that during his career in England he had to contend with many changes in the ruling orders. His active career from 1621 to 1655 covered the reigns of James and Charles, the Civil War with its complicated, elusive and divided loyalties, the Commonwealth, and the early years of Cromwell's Protectorate. It does not need much imagination to realise how difficult it must have been in such circumstances to retain a settled policy when by the nature of things, and of the times, such policy was so dependent upon personal favours and friendships. The story of Sir Cornelius Vermuyden and the Great Level would have been very different had there been no Civil War, and had Charles been able to continue with his undertaking of 1638. And not only would the story have been different, but in all probability the scheme of drainage also because it is felt that the scheme completed in 1653 was substantially different from the original ideas of Vermuyden. That state of affairs was brought about by the 'comptrollment', of the Adventurers after 1649, and it is a reasonable supposition that the King would have proved much more compliant and would have given his Director of Works a much freer hand. Presuming, of course, that the money had been available. That in itself is a very dubious presumption and it is somewhat unprofitable speculation to attempt to picture what might have happened if this or that had, or had not, occurred.

Whatever may be the verdict on the personal character of Vermuyden, or on his technical achievements, it is difficult to withhold some admiration for the manner in which he dealt with the difficulties of changing political circumstances, and overcame all the obstacles set in his path. Assuming that his first arrival in England was in 1621, and assuming also that he came as the agent of Joachim Liens and his associates, one of the most remarkable features of his career is the dominant personal position which he had built up in the space of nine years when, in 1630, he was first engaged by Francis, Earl of Bedford, on the Great Level. Of course, when he arrived in England, he did not do so as a friendless stranger. His connection with Joachim Liens was quite enough to establish him, not only in the circles of the Court, where, as we know, interest in the financial possibilities of Fen drainage was so great, but also with the comparatively large settlement of Netherlanders already at that time in England. These he soon left behind and carved out for himself a niche from which no amount of denigration can depose him.

The mystery which has hitherto surrounded the life of Vermuyden after the year 1655 has been largely due to a placid acceptance of the fact that he was 'the man who drained the Fens' and the desire to leave it at that, so that when the Fens were drained, to all intents and purposes, in 1655, that was to most the end of the Vermuyden story. There has never been until the present time any attempt to probe into the mystery of the later years. That the Vermuyden family did fade away after 1655 may be concluded from Abraham de la Pryme's letter of enquiry to Mr. Parolle, but in actual fact their activities were not noticed because these were transferred from the land drainage world, with which the Vermuyden name has always been associated, to other fields less conspicuous. As will be shown later, Sir Cornelius himself was engaged in other very different occupations, while the Chancery Suits arising from the ownership of the Dovegang Lead Mine at Wirksworth provide vital and illuminating evidence of the complicated, and sometimes not too edifying, transactions associated with that venture. Both Cornelius the eldest son and John the second surviving son come into this particular story, while Cornelius is shown from other evidence to have been a man of some accomplishment and standing. Indeed, it is largely through the children of Sir Cornelius and Lady Katherine, who throughout remains a shadowy figure, that we are able to piece together something of the father in his later years.

Earlier on we have briefly commented on the birth of the first Vermuyden children and it will, perhaps, at this stage be best to record details of all the children of whom it has been possible to discover positive evidence. These are as follows:

1. Sarah,	Born in Holland, ca. 1624(?)	
2. Cornelius.	Baptised St. Botolph's, Bishopsgate, 19th March, 1626.	
3. Catherine.	,,	Dutch Reformed Church, Austin Friars, 22nd January, 1626/7.
4. Thomas.	,,	St. Dionys Backchurch, London, 15th June, 1628.
5. John.	,,	St. Dionys Backchurch, 8th October, 1629.
6. Gyles.	,,	Great Abington, Cambs., 30th September, 1631.
7. Adrianna.	,,	St. Dionys Backchurch, 18th January, 1632/3.
8. Bartholomew.	,,	Dutch Reformed Church, 21st August, 1634.
9. Anna	,,	Dutch Reformed Church, 26th July, 1635.

10. Mary. Baptised St. Dionys Backchurch, 21st July, 1636.
11. Charles. ,, St. Dionys Backchurch, 22nd December, 1637.
12. Susannah. ,, St. Dionys Backchurch, 28th December, 1638.
13. Deborah (No date or place of birth or baptism traceable.)

Thus there are no details available of the baptismal dates of either Sarah or of Deborah but, as will become clear later, there is ample evidence for the existence of these as children of Sir Cornelius, while the suggestion that Sarah was born in Holland is based only on the statement of Korthals-Altes who produces no evidence to support it. On the other hand, in December 1635, Christopher Clitherow, Lord Mayor of London, was presenting a certificate to the Privy Council, 'of strangers born beyond seas' residing in the Ward of Langbourne, and in the Parish of St. Dionys Backchurch we find the entry 'Sir Cornelius Vermuyden born in . . . Zeeland. He hath seven children all born in this parish'.[1] At that date it will be seen that Sir Cornelius had had nine children born to him of whom, however, only seven survived. Gyles, the son baptised at Great Abington, a village a few miles south of Cambridge, must, presumably, have been born at or near that village when Lady Vermuyden was accompanying her husband on one of his many visits to the Great Level, but the unfortunate child only survived a few months because on 21st February, 1631/2 we find in the register of St. Dionys Backchurch a record of the burial of 'Gyles Bermuden [*sic*] son of Cornelius Vermuden'. In the register of the same church there is recorded the burial on some unspecified date between 9th June and 22nd August, 1635, of 'Thomas Vermuyden', and another of the same name on 1st May, 1635, and while in neither case is any description, or relationship to Sir Cornelius, given it must be concluded that one of these was the son baptised on 15th June, 1628, if only for the reason that, although the names of the other children recur in later years, there is never any mention of Thomas Vermuyden. But the query that is raised by the Lord Mayor's certificate is that if, as he said, Sir Cornelius Vermuyden at that time had seven children 'all born in this parish' then this number must include Sarah, and the suggestion that she was born in Holland must be wrong.

By the year 1635, the year of the London Visitation, Sir Cornelius had, as we know, severed all connection as far as was in his power with Hatfield Chase and was fully committed to the work in the Great Level. By this year also he had, in company with Sir Robert Heath, begun that connection with the lead mine at Wirksworth, a connection which was to influence the Vermuyden family long after Sir Cornelius was dead. The Wirksworth

[1] *Cal. State Papers Dom. Charles I,* CCV, 591.

mine could provide material for a story of Sir Cornelius entirely divorced from his land reclamation work and the undertaking there appears to have begun in an atmosphere of dispute, to have continued in the same strain for some sixty years at least, and thus to have produced the succession of suits in the Court of Chancery from which it is possible to build up the whole story. As early as May 1635, Heath was writing to Secretary Windebank telling him that he had 'received notice of the King's pleasure on Sunday next at the council board to hear the cause touching the lead mine in Derbyshire whereunto George Sayer pretends, or more truly Lord Dover, and some other in the name of Sayer, he being dead, pretend against the writer and his partner Sir Cornelius Vermuyden'.[1] It is believed that Heath and Vermuyden had the full support of Charles in the matter of the Wirksworth mine, and in April 1638 the King was writing to the Corporation of Derby in the following terms.

'The King understanding that the Bailiffs and Burgesses of Derby with the rest of the Corporation are owners of a house on the Darwent side desires that they will make choice to be their tenant Sir Cornelius Vermuyden who with his partners had undertaken a work very acceptable to the King about the works at Warksworth [*sic*] and to make the river Darwent to be navigable till it falls into the Trent.'[2]

Whether Vermuyden ever occupied this house, or whether he ever carried out improvement works on the Derwent, is not known, but the letter certainly indicates a friendly interest in the Wirksworth undertaking.

One of the very few circumstances in which the name of Lady Katherine Vermuyden is mentioned is in connection with the membership of herself and her husband of the Dutch Reformed Church of which, apparently, they became members in their early years in England. Korthals-Altes says that after 16th December, 1638, Lady Katherine had 'dissociated herself from active participation in all events concerning the Dutch Church' but even if their membership of the church had lasted as long as this, their adherence must have been somewhat tenuous because, as will have been seen, of the ten children baptised in London, only three appear in the register of the Dutch Reformed Church. As late as 1646 this church appears to have been attempting to exercise its authority over the Vermuydens and on 12th February of that year Sir Cornelius was writing in the following terms.

'As the matter of the large fens was dealt with today I was unable to appear before the consistory, but as to the baptism of my child, I regard the baptism of children as an ordinance of God. Nor did I scruple to present

[1] *Cal. State Papers Dom. Charles I*, CCLXXXIX. 87.

[2] *H.M.C. 12th Report.*, App. Part II. Coke MSS. i. 180.

it to the Dutch community but as my wife (though otherwise sound on this point) requested some delay, I consented, as she felt inclined to have our child baptised in the English church, this being a common custom . . .'[1]

It is difficult to determine the child to which this letter refers. The conclusion is, however, that it was Deborah the youngest child who may have been born in or about the year 1644, but it is difficult to appreciate why there should have been this question over the baptism of a child in 1646 when there had been six others in earlier years baptised in the church of St. Dionys Backchurch, and one at St. Botolph's, Bishopsgate. What we do know is that 'the matter of the large fens' refers to the meetings of the Committee of the House of Commons under Pelham's chairmanship, and it may be that Sir Cornelius had been prevented by the pressure of this business from replying to the letters from the Dutch Church.

[1] Quoted by KORTHALS-ALTES, *op. cit.*, p. 62.

CHAPTER EIGHTEEN

Vermuyden's financial state. His children's marriages. His son Cornelius's friendship with Christiaan Huygens, his own relations with Jacob Cats. The Chancery Suits. The 'Fairmeadow Legend' destroyed. Death of Vermuyden. Date and place of his burial.

THERE is no doubt that Sir Cornelius Vermuyden during the early years of his association with the Great Level was living in a state, if not of affluence, at least of solid comfort, and there is also no doubt that his fortunes were founded largely on the Hatfield Chase undertaking. The fact that most of the participants in this undertaking in comparison made nothing out of it may appear at first sight to be discreditable to Vermuyden although it may also be looked upon as a tribute to his perspicacity and astuteness. In the year 1638 the rental of the house which he occupied in the parish of St. Dionys Backchurch was £60 per annum,[1] a large sum indeed in those days, indicating to some degree his style of living. This, of course, was the time of the heyday of his career, when King Charles had declared himself undertaker for the draining of the Great Level and when, no doubt, Sir Cornelius was enjoying the full benefits of the Royal favour. This phase was not to last long and with the outbreak of the Civil War in 1642 his fortune must have undergone a radical change. Indeed the seven years between 1642 and the passing of the Pretended Act in May 1649 may have been a period of some financial difficulties. Even if he did possess 4,000 acres of undrained land in Sedgmoor, and perhaps, still retained his ownership of his part of Malvern Chase, even if, also, he had secured parcels of land in the Great Level, these could have been of little income value during the troublous times of the Civil War. The lead mines at Wirksworth may have continued to provide some considerable contribution and it is significant that, although he eventually was compelled in later years to dispose of a lot of his land in the Great Level, he steadfastly retained both his interest in those mines and his ownership of the Sedgmoor acres up to the end of his days.

[1] *Nieuw Nederlandsch Biografisch Woordenboek*, Vol. VII, 1251. Leiden, 1927.

How much land in the Great Level Sir Cornelius had at one time owned is somewhat uncertain. He had, of course, the 4,000 acres allotted to him under the terms of the agreement which he signed with the Adventurers in December 1649, but in February 1655, a suit was filed against him in the Chancery Court by one John Gibbon and others in which it was stated that 'Sir Cornelius Vermuyden of London, Knt. and Merchant, or other for him, were about 5 years since seized of 5,800 acres of land in the Great Level of the Fens'. Presumably, on the security of these lands he had borrowed from Gibbon and his friends the sum of £30,000 and, according to his accusers, had been in arrears for his drainage taxes to the tune of £900 in the years 1653, 1654, and 1655. But, in addition, it was alleged that Sir Cornelius had 'for many years past traded as a Merchant by way of Exchange rechange—bartering and chevissance . . . and about 4 years since had become Bankrupt.'[1]

How much of all this is true it is difficult to prove, but it is interesting to note that William, Earl of Bedford, Robert Henley, Wm. Say, John Latch and Anthony Samwell, five of the defendants who were joined in the suit, entered a Plea and Demurrer in which they said that Sir Cornelius Vermuyden was not as yet declared bankrupt' and, turning to the attack, asserted that John Gibbon had been outlawed for debt in 1648 'and was and is convicted, and was also outlawed for debt in London in 1651, which debts are not paid.'[2]

This suit may not prove anything, but it may indicate that by the beginning of 1655 Vermuyden was experiencing some financial trouble, and although Gibbon may have been at least, unreliable, it is possible that there was a basis of truth in the accusations. One interesting fact which appears to emerge is that Sir Cornelius had been trading 'as a Merchant' for some years while still employed as Director of Works in the Great Level, and as the date on which the suit was filed, 12th February, was only eight days after the date on which Sir Cornelius attended his last meeting of the Adventurers on 4th February, it would not be stretching probability too far to see some connection between the suit and the severance of Vermuyden's connection with the Bedford Level Adventurers.

It is quite possible that in the years immediately following his break with the Adventurers his fortunes, and his income, may have declined, but there is no justification for imagining that he ever sank into a state of poverty. The story once current that he died in the poorhouse at Belton near Hatfield, has long ago been discarded and can now, in the light of present knowledge,

[1] Chancery Proc. before 1714. Bridges. C.5.267/8.
[2] *Ibid.*

be proved to have been one of those far-fetched imaginative stories which have so often in the past been linked with the name of Vermuyden. It is conceivable that the restriction of Sir Cornelius's income after 1655, and that state of affairs is merely assumption, may have led to a less ostentatious mode of life in his household than that which had prevailed in earlier years. If he ever had been in a penurious state it is likely that he would have sold his land in Sedgmoor and his interest in the Dovegang mine at Wirksworth. We know, in fact, that he did not and, furthermore, the social conditions to which his children attained, or at least, those of whom we have particulars, tend further to disprove the complete financial and social collapse of the father.

Deborah, the youngest of the Vermuyden children, made, perhaps, the best marriage of them all, for in 1666 at the age of twenty-two, if our assumption of 1644 as the year of her birth is correct, she was married to Sir Francis Bickley, of Attleborough, co. Norfolk, third holder of the baronetcy originally conferred in 1661 on his grandfather, Francis Bickley, a prosperous draper of Budge Row in the City of London, and of Dalston. But poor Lady Deborah had a short married life. She bore her husband three children. The eldest, also christened Francis on 28th January, 1667, eventually succeeded to the baronetcy, but on 6th March, 1669, Deborah died in childbirth.[1] In Mortimer's Chapel of the church of Attleborough there is a tablet in the floor to her memory, and on this, if the worn lettering can be deciphered, can be seen the words:

> SUB HOC MARMORE IN SPEM BEATAE RESURRECTIONIS RECONDUNTUR . . . DEBORAE BICKLEY, FILIAE CORNELIUS VERMUYDEN MILITIS.

The solitary memorial to a member of the family of Sir Cornelius Vermuyden which has yet been found.

Charles, the youngest son, was a student of Grays Inn, in 1657, being entered as the son of 'Sir Charles [*sic*] of Westminster, Kt'. He graduated B.A. from Christ Church, Oxford in 1661 and became a licentiate of the college of physicians in 1662.[2] At some subsequent date he married Mary Upton, a member of a well-to-do Devonshire family, and on his death in 1673 she married again, becoming the fourth wife of Sir John Maynard, Serjeant-at-Law, and when Sir John died in 1690, Mary, still persevering and obviously a woman of charm, and, possibly, of fortune, married Henry, sixth Earl of Suffolk, as his second wife, dying finally in 1720.[3]

[1] COCKAYNE, *Complete Baronetage.*
[2] *Alumni Oxoniensis.*
[3] *Notes and Queries*, 8th Series, iv. 152. LE NEVE, *Knights*, p. 117.

Susannah married on 2nd June, 1663, George Liddell, son of Sir Francis Liddell of Redheugh, co. Palatine of Durham.[1] Catherine married Thomas Babbington of Somersham, Huntingdonshire, an essentially Fenland town only a few miles from the head of the twin Bedford Rivers at Earith. He was the second son of Thomas Babington, Esquire, Lord of the Manor of Rothley Temple, Leicestershire, a member of a family of ancient lineage tracing their descent back to the early years of the fifteenth century.[3] Catherine was buried at Rothley Temple on 1st July, 1669.

From these details of the marriages of Deborah, Charles and Catherine it seems apparent that these were not the marriages of the children of an impecunious naturalised Dutchman who had been dismissed from the services of the Bedford Level Corporation for petty peculation. The dates of Deborah's marriage, of Charles's graduation and marriage, and of Catherine's marriage, were all in the lifetime of Sir Cornelius because, as we shall establish later, he died in the year 1677, and it can be assumed, therefore, that even if there had been some shrinkage in his fortune after the year 1655, he still retained something, if not all, of his social position.

Doubtless both Deborah and Catherine owed their marriages to the work in the Great Level, and the friendships which had grown up from that work between their father and the Bickleys and the Babbingtons. Sarah the eldest daughter likewise owed her marriage presumably to the ownership of the land in Sedgmoor because she married one John Blake of Huish Episcopi, co. Somerset, and although we know very little of her life in the early years it has been possible to establish that on the death of John Blake she married as her second husband Andrew Ruell, of whom we know nothing except that he appears to have been a somewhat cautious individual. That we shall explain later.

There is no intention here of going into the details of the lives of the children of Sir Cornelius except for the purpose of elucidating some point in connection with the life of Sir Cornelius himself. It might be interesting on some future occasion to follow out the career of Cornelius the son of whom so far little has been said. The question of his possible service in the Parliamentary Army has already been discussed, as has also that of the presenting of his scheme for the draining of the Great Level to Pelham's Committee. He married Anne, daughter of Sir Compton Reade, Bart., another example of a marriage of some social importance, and there is little doubt that he was a man of accomplishment and position. He certainly at one time owned land in the Great Level, and he was elected a Conservator to the Corpora-

[1] *London Marriage Licences*, (CHESTER), p. 845.

[2] BURKE, *History of the Landed Gentry*, iv. 517. 1838.

tion in 1665, and, what is perhaps of more significance, he became a founder member of the Royal Society in 1663 and as such was on intimate terms with the leading scientific men of his day. Christiaan Huygens, the Dutch mathematician was elected on the same day and two years earlier in his Journal for the year 1661, when he was in England, records visits which he made to Gresham's College and to Windsor in company with Cornelius Vermuyden, Sir Robert Moray, Lord Brouncker, Alexander Bruce, Earl of Kincardine, and others. Cornelius certainly presented two papers to the Royal Society, one, incidentally, on a method of reviving men suffocated in coal mines by putting their heads into fresh earth, and in the year 1685, in company with Christopher Cratford of London, he was granted a licence by Charles II for the supplying of 'Fresh Water by channels and pipes or any other lawful ways or means . . . towards our Town and Garrison of Portsmouth'.[1] At one time he lived in 'Channel Rowe, Westminster, where he had a great house, kept many servants and lived in a plentifull manner.'[2]

All these details tend to show that Cornelius was a man of some considerable importance, but in themselves they are not really relevant to the life of Sir Cornelius except in two respects. Firstly they help to emphasise further the standing of the son in the lifetime of the father, and secondly, and most important, they lead us directly to the ownership of the lands in Sedgmoor and of the lead mines at Wirksworth, a subject in which, as we shall see later, Sarah plays her inconspicuous but valuable part.

The mention in the journal of Christian Huygens of his visits to Windsor in company with Cornelius Vermuyden indicates that a friendship must have existed between the two men, a friendship having its origin in the friendship between their two fathers, Constantijn Huygens and Sir Cornelius Vermuyden. This point is of some significance because the latter friendship, or it may have been only a business association, dated from 1627 at the time of the Hatfield Chase undertaking, and was particularly concerned with the financial arrangements for that undertaking.

Jacob Cats, it will be recalled, had taken a minor share in the Hatfield Chase undertaking, along with his nephew Leonard and members of the van Valckenburgh family. Now Cats's ventures in the reclamation of the flooded lands in the Staats Vlanderen after the year 1611 had all proved financially successful and in many cases the whole of the capital outlay had been recovered in the course of a year. It was on the basis of these results and in anticipation of similar results to be obtained from Hatfield Chase that

[1] *Patent Roll*, 36. Car. II. part 8. No. 13.
[2] *Chancery Proc. before* 1714. Reynardson. C. 9. 142/10.

Cats had induced his friend Constantijn Huygens to participate in the venture there. The hopeful prophecies of Jacob Cats, however, were not fulfilled and the eventual unfortunate financial results of the Hatfield Chase undertaking created some animosity between Cats and Vermuyden, and, doubtless, between the latter and the other participants. The full financial implications of Hatfield Chase did not become completely apparent for some years and it is possible that in 1629 Vermuyden still commanded sufficient confidence in the Netherlands for him to have the intention of financing his proposed undertaking in the Great Level with the aid of his countrymen there. How far the differences between Vermuyden and Cats extended it is difficult to say. The former in the administrative and promotion work associated with his ventures was undoubtedly capable, calculating, shrewd and astute, qualifications just as essential to personal commercial success in the seventeenth century as they are today. And no more reprehensible. Jacob Cats, a shrewd man of business himself, was fully aware of this, and the question arising out of this set of circumstances is this.

If Sir Cornelius Vermuyden had been stigmatised as a swindler by Jacob Cats, as has sometimes been suggested, and hence by Constantijn Huygens, over the Hatfield Chase undertaking would any friendship have existed, such as is indicated by the Windsor visits, between the two sons, Cornelius and Christiaan, when, it must be remembered, Sir Cornelius Vermuyden himself was still living in London? It is a question incapable of a conclusive answer, but it would not be unreasonable to conclude that there was no suggestion of dishonesty attached to the financial failure at Hatfield, and thus, although there may have been recriminations on the part of the disappointed speculators, there was no break in their friendship with Sir Cornelius, or at least between him and Constantijn Huygens.

When Cornelius the son died, if he was not in a state of complete insolvency, his financial affairs were in some considerable confusion, because, perhaps, of the 'plentifull manner' in which he had at one time lived. But if it had not been for the insolvency of Cornelius we might not have had incontrovertible evidence of his ownership at the time of his death in 1693 of the Sedgmoor and Wirksworth properties and, therefore, of the fact that his father had not disposed of them.

The story of the Chancery Suits from which this evidence is obtained is too long to relate in detail, but briefly the story is this. Cornelius died intestate and one Thomas Lediard as principal creditor applied for Letters of Administration which were granted, but revoked in the following year when Sarah Vermuyden, or Sarah Ruell as she had become by then, successfully applied for the administration to be granted to her. Lediard filed a list of sums owing to him by Cornelius on the latter's death, which with interest were stated to amount to a total of over £3,000. Then followed suit after suit in which not only Sarah, but also her husband Andrew Ruell, her son by her first marriage, Joseph Blake, and her brother Bartholomew were also joined. Andrew Ruell found that in marrying Sarah he had involved himself in more than he had ever bargained for and proceeded not only to deny that he was concerned in any of the legal processes, but safeguarded himself by disappearing into the country. Sarah herself had to admit that 'she and her servant board with her son Joseph Blake who lives in Finch Lane near the Royal Exchange, and that her husband is in the country, but she knows not the name of the place'. A very prudent man.

The lands in Somerset are frequently cited in the suits as part of the assets of the late Cornelius, and Lediard asserted that Cornelius had told him that the 4,000 acres were worth '20/- an acre annually'. The dispute over the lead mines at Wirksworth concerned the supposed intention of Cornelius shortly before his death, to dispose of these to one Francis Gell for the sum of £2,000 plus a further £3,000 from 'the first profits raised out of the said mines by the said Gell'. There was, incidentally, a further suit entered against Sarah as administrator by the executors of Thomas Browne, the late, vicar of Wirksworth, on the accusation that Cornelius had for many years failed to pay 'the Tenth of Lead Ore' which was 'for time out of mind a customary duty paid to the vicar'.

The story behind these suits is an interesting one, the interest lying more with the Vermuyden family than with Sir Cornelius. But they give incontrovertible proof that during his lifetime Sir Cornelius never disposed of his Sedgmoor estates nor of his interest in the Dovegang mine at Wirksworth.

Apart from that faint gleam there is little to enlighten us on the life of Sir Cornelius after the year 1656 until his death in 1677. The latter date is one which the present writer has recently established, and the manner of its establishment will be described later, while until now it has been generally accepted that he died on 6th April, 1683.[1] It is, perhaps, of interest to trace the steps by which this entirely false assumption was built up into an accepted fact, and thus created what might be termed the 'Fairmeadow Legend'. This is a curious story which owes its origin to the existence of a comparatively unknown individual named Cornelius Fairmeadow, a completely unwitting actor in this comedy of errors. He had, indeed, been dead some two hundred and thirty years before the curtain rose.

Of this Cornelius Fairmeadow we know very little, but we do know that on 30th May, 1624, the Privy Council granted 'A pass for Cornelius Fair-

[1] See article on Vermuyden in *Dictionary of National Biography*.

meadow, John Stonehouse and Edmund Wingate, to travel into forraine partes for the space of three years with their servants and provisions, not prohibited, with the proviso not to go to Rome'.[1] A similar pass had, indeed, been granted on 27th May of the previous year to cover a period of only four months.[2] Whether this travel was for private purposes or whether on some business of the King's is not yet known, but it is, perhaps, significant that some eighteen months after the expiration of the second pass Fairmeadow was knighted by Charles at Windsor, the record reading as follows:

'1628. Sept. 25. Cornelius Fairmeadow, a gentleman pensioner, of Feltham, Middl.'[3]

Sometime or other, the date has not yet been established, Cornelius Fairmeadow married Dionysia Stonehouse who can be identified with some assurance. She was the grand-daughter of George Stonehouse, of Little Peckham in Kent, one of the Clerks of the Green Cloth to Queen Elizabeth, and a daughter of his son William, created baronet in 1628, by his second marriage to Elizabeth Powell. Dionysia by her marriage to Cornelius Fairmeadow had a daughter Elizabeth who, on 31st August, 1647, married Sir Thomas Peneystone the 2nd baronet, and if we assume that Elizabeth was about eighteen years of age at the time of her marriage, then Dionysia may have married Cornelius Fairmeadow sometime around the year 1627 or 1628 on his return from 'forraine parts'. Elizabeth Peneystone had two sons; Thomas, who succeeded to the baronetcy on the death of his father in May, 1674, and Fairmeadow, who became the 4th baronet on the death of his brother Thomas in 1679. Sir Fairmeadow Peneystone himself died in December 1705, without any heir, the baronetcy thus becoming extinct. Elizabeth's husband, Sir Thomas Peneystone, the 2nd baronet, died in May 1674, and was buried on the 29th at Cornwall, co. Oxford, and some six days later, on the 3rd July, Elizabeth herself was laid to rest in the same grave.[4]

A lot of these details may appear to be completely irrelevant, but they are given in order to substantiate as far as possible the marriage of Dionysia Stonehouse to Cornelius Fairmeadow, for which, indeed, the appearance of the name John Stonehouse in the pass granted by the Privy Council provides additional confirmation. John Stonehouse was the brother of

[1] Acts of the Privy Council, June 1623 to March 1625. p. 222.
[2] *Ibid.* July 1621 to June 1623, p, 504.
[3] SHAW, *Knights of England*, 1906.
[4] COKAYNE, *Complete Baronetage*, 1900.
BENTHAM, *Baronetage*, i. 317. 1801.

Dionysia and succeeded to his father's baronetcy in February 1631/2, but died five months later in June 1632 at the age of thirty-one. And what more suitable companion for Fairmeadow on his continental trip that his future brother-in-law?

It may be asked, what has all this to do with Cornelius Vermuyden? The answer to that question is that there was, apparently, no connection for nearly two hundred and fifty years, but that at the end of that period by wishful thinking and fallacious arguments the foundations of the 'Fairmeadow Legend' were laid. And so soundly were they laid that the 'legend' has persisted to the present day.

In the year 1877 a correspondent in *Notes and Queries* wrote that 'In an "Act of Naturalisation of certain Noblemen and Gentlemen of England" passed by the Scottish Parliament in 1633 (Act. P. Scottl. V. 58) occurs the name Sir Cornelius Pharmedo', and suggested that 'we have in the disguise of a quaint Scottish spelling Sir Cornelius Vermuyden, the eminent Dutch engineer', although he was frank enough to admit that there was no evidence to show that Vermuyden had ever been in Scotland.[1] Admittedly there may have been some difficulty in the seventeenth century, even in England, in deciding upon the true pronunciation of the name 'Vermuyden'. Indeed that difficulty exists today and unless the true Dutch pronunciation has been heard and mastered there are many spoken variants bearing little relation to the truth. But in spite of this, the present writer has never heard the name pronounced in any way corresponding to the spelling 'Pharmedo'. This to the unprejudiced eye and ear is clearly a phonetic rendering of 'Fairmeadow', or one of its variants, 'Fairmedoe' or 'Farmedow' for example. Clearly the correspondent in *Notes and Queries* was unaware of the existence of Cornelius Fairmeadow and jumped to too hasty conclusions with results that he could never have foreseen.

The story thus started quickly gathered momentum and some years later, in the absence of any details of the death of Vermuyden, he was identified with the 'Cornelius Fairmeadow, *eques auratus*' who, it was stated, was buried at St. Martin-in-the-Fields on 6th April, 1683, it being also asserted that letters of administration were granted to Dionysia his widow on the 20th of that month.[2] By this time the story was firmly established, 1683 being accepted as the year of Vermuyden's death, and working entirely on these assumptions it was also stated that he had had a daughter Elizabeth (the Elizabeth who married Sir Thomas Peneystone) and that, at some unspecified date, he had married as his second wife Dionysia Stonehouse.[3]

[1] *Notes and Queries, 5th Series* vii. 429.

[2] *Notes and Queries, 6th Series,* ii, 35, 8th Series, iii, 478

[3] D.N.B. *Notes and Queries, 8th Series,* iv, 152.

It all seemed a very plausible story and the assumed date of Sir Cornelius Vermuyden's death in 1683 was quite possible, but there were one or two points which had been overlooked. The recorded details of Cornelius Fairmeadow's knighthood have already been quoted and those for the knighthood of Cornelius Vermuyden read as follows:

1628–9 Jan. 6. Cornelius Vermuyden, of Hadfield, co. Yorks. [At Whitehall].[1]

It was somewhat difficult for the adherents to the 'Fairmeadow Legend' to explain the apparent double conferment. In fact no explanation was given. It was blandly asserted that Cornelius Vermuyden was knighted on 25th September, 1628 *or* on 6th January, 1628/9, but there was no solution to the mystery of why the ceremony should have been performed once at Windsor and once at Whitehall, or why Vermuyden was correctly described as 'of Hadfield [Hatfield] co. Yorks' in January and in September as 'a gentleman pensioner of Feltham, Midx.' which he never was.

An examination of the register of St. Martin-in-the Fields discloses the following entry of burial under the date 6th April, 1638, *not* 1683.

'Cornelius Farmado, *eques auratus*.'

In the Prerogative Court of Canterbury, Act Book, 1636–38, there is the following entry:

'20 April, 1638, Administration of the goods of Sir Cornelius Fairmeadow, late of St. Martin-in-the Fields, co. Midx, Knt., granted to Dame Dionisie Fairmedoe the Relict.'

And thus the whole 'Fairmeadow Legend' collapses. It was founded on wishful thinking in relation to the 'Quaint Scottish spelling' and it was kept alive for many years by a curious transposition of the figures '3' and '8' in the date 1683. Sir Cornelius Vermuyden did not marry Dionysia Stonehouse, he did not have a daughter Elizabeth. He certainly did not die in 1638 when Cornelius Fairmeadow died.

The first clue to the real date of his death is contained in the Chancery Suits resulting from the dispute over the estate of Cornelius the younger. In these suits there are two conflicting statements. Thomas Lediard in the first suit, in referring to the Dovegang mine, says that 'Sir C. Vermuyden, Knt., was according to the same custom seised of the mine and died so seised 40 years since'. In the suit filed by the executors of Thomas Browne, vicar of Wirksworth, it is again stated that 'Sir Cornelius Vermuyden, Knt.,

[1] SHAW'S *Knights of England. Op. cit.*

father of the said Cornelius Vermuyden, who died so seised about 40 years ago'. Now both these suits were filed in the year 1694 which would mean that Sir Cornelius died in about 1654. That we know is out of the question. The confusion which existed in the minds of these plaintiffs probably arose from the fact that Sir Cornelius Vermuyden assigned his interest in the Dovegang mine to his son Cornelius sometime about 1651. This is proved by the petition of Cornelius dated 23rd April, 1651, for 'allowance of his title of the lot and cope of the Dovegang' where he states that 'Sir Cornelius assigned his interest to the petitioner.'[1]

The true facts are given by the children Bartholomew and Sarah. Bartholomew in his answer to Lediard's suit says that the Dovegang mine descended to Cornelius 'on the death of this Defendant's father Sir Cornelius Vermuyden, who was seised of same and died about 16 years ago'. Sarah's statement is that Sir Cornelius 'died so seised . . . about 16 or 17 years since'. Again the date of both these statements is 1694 which makes the date of the death of Sir Cornelius about 1677–78, and it would be fair to assume that the children knew the date of their father's death.

The second clue is contained in the London Marriage Licenses for the marriage of Susannah Vermuyden to George Liddell where Susannah is stated to be the 'daur of Sir Cornelius Vermuyden of Channel Row, City of Westminster', and where also it is stated that 'both fathers were consenting' to the marriage. Thus clearly Sir Cornelius was alive and living in Westminster on 2nd June, 1663, the date of the marriage.

The third clue is provided by the Chancery Suit which one Edward Perry filed against Cornelius Vermuyden the son, who in his answer of 27th April, 1672 stated that he was 'son and heir apparent of Sir Cornelius Vermuyden, Knt. but not the son and heir (the said Sir C.V. being yet alive and in being).'[2]

And so in the end was found in the register of the church of St. Margaret, Westminster, the record of the burial of 'S^r^. Cornel^s^ Vermooden' on 15th October, 1677, and that simple entry, which has taken so many years to trace, gives us conclusively the last record of that remarkable man. By 1677 he had reached the age of eighty-seven, and presumably, he died in the 'great House in Channel Row, Westminster', close to the church of St. Margaret. Full of years he was and full of accomplishments, yet, perhaps, with a mind filled with disappointment at the thought that he had not quite achieved all that he had set out to do. The drainage of the Great Level had been his main aim, and that he had accomplished, but Sedgmoor, where for

[1] *Proc. Committee for Compounding, 1643–1660.* Part IV. 2775.

[2] *Chancery Proc. before* 1714. BRIDGES. C. 5. 537-92.

so long he had retained his lands, had in the end eluded him. From the year 1621 when he first viewed the Great Level until 1677 is a long space of time. For thirty-five of those years he served England well, better than his contemporaries and successors realised, or would admit, and hence for the remaining twenty-one years he remained neglected in the background of history. At least, that is how it appears on the surface. Perhaps Vermuyden preferred it that way. Perhaps by the year 1656 when he had failed in his attempts to gain permission to drain Sedgmoor he had had quite enough of the land drainage business, and preferred to spend the rest of his days resigned to quiet retirement in Westminster. On the other hand, his occupation as a merchant, and his business of 'exchange, rechange and chevissance' may have given him, and his mind, all the employment which he desired. But one fact must not be overlooked. His relations with the Protector Cromwell had extended over a number of years, and may in the end have become intimate and confidential. With the death of Cromwell in 1658, and the Restoration in 1660, Sir Cornelius may have found it politic to remain in the background in spite of his apparently neutral conduct during the Civil War. Furthermore, there is no denying that from the year 1656 onwards there were distinct signs that all was not well with the drainage system there, even if, as we know now, the deterioration could not be laid directly on Vermuyden's shoulders.

His beginning was in the comparative obscurity of a little township in the province of Zeeland, and the finish, as far as we know now, in a somewhat unmerited obscurity, until today a more just judgement brings him forth as one who deserves well of posterity, whatever may have been his personal character.

Sir Cornelius Vermuyden looks out from his portrait by van Miereveld with that determination which carried him so far and through so much, and with something of that aggressiveness which, perhaps, served him well in the earlier years, but later contributed so largely to the failure of his friendships. Above all there is something of disdain in his look as though he were challenging the present to question his greatness, in spite of all his human frailities. And that is something which the present day cannot justifiably do.

BIBLIOGRAPHY

Details of publications and authorities consulted have been given as footnotes throughout the text, but in order to facilitate reference these have been summarised below.

(A). GENERAL SOURCES

Acts of the Privy Council.
Calendar of State Papers Domestic. Elizabeth.
do. James I.
do. Charles I.
do. Commonwealth.
Proc. of the Committee of Compounding with Delinquents, 1643–1660.
British Record Soc. *Publications: Marriage Licenses*, etc.
Harleian Soc. *Publications:* Church Registers.
Chancery Proceedings: Public Record Office.
Historical Manuscripts Commission, *Reports.*
Journals of the House of Lords.
Journals of the House of Commons.
Dictionary of National Biography.
Nieuw Nederlandsch Biografisch Woordenboek, 1927.
Fen Office Documents.
Middle Level Commissioners Documents.
Proc. Cambridge Antiquarian Society.
Trans. Royal Historical Society.
English Historical Review.
Victoria County Histories.
BURKE's *Complete Peerage.*
Notes and Queries.
Fenland Notes and Queries.
BENTHAM's *Baronetage*, 1801.

(B). BOOKS

W. CAMDEN, *Britain, a Chorographical Description of the most flourishing Kingdoms of England, Scotland and Ireland.* 7th ed. 1610.

JOHN PERRY, *An Account of the Stopping of Daggenham Breach*, 1721.
T. BADESLADE, *A History of the . . . Navigation of the Port of King's Lynn*, 1725.
THOMAS BIRCH, *A collection of State Papers of John Thurloe, Esq.*, 1742.
N. KINDERLEY, *The Ancient and Present State of the Navigation of the Town of Lyn etc.*, 1751.
P. MORANT, *The History and Antiquities of the County of Essex*, 1768.
W. DUGDALE, *The History of Embanking and Draining.* 2nd ed., 1772.
T. BIRCH (ed.), *The Diary of Thomas Burton Esq., . . . from 1656 to 1659*, 1828.
JOSEPH HUNTER, *South Yorkshire*, 1828.
S. WELLS, *History of the Drainage of the Great Level of the Fens*, 1830.
J. H. WIFFEN, *Memoirs of the House of Russell*, 1833.
W. B. STONEHOUSE, *The History and Topography of the Isle of Axholme*, 1839.
S. SMILES, *Lives of the Engineers*, 1861.
S. B. SKERTCHLEY, *The Geology of the Fenland*, 1877.
S. H. MILLER AND S. B. SKERTCHLEY, *The Fenland Past and Present*, 1878.
S. R. GARDINER, *History of England*, 1884.
History of the Commonwealth and Protectorate, 1897.
A. KINGSTON, *East Anglia and the Great Civil War*, 1897.
S. C. LOMAS (ed.), *Letters and Speeches of Oliver Cromwell*, 1904.
W. A. SHAW, *The Knights of England*, 1906.
F. A. HIBBERT, *The Dissolution of the Monasteries*, 1910.
CYRIL FOX, *The Archaeology of the Cambridge Region*, 1923.
J. KORTHALS-ALTES, *Sir Cornelius Vermuyden*, 1925.
G. SCOTT THOMSON, *Two Centuries of Family History*, 1930.
Family Background, 1949.
H. C. DARBY, *The Mediaeval Fenland*, 1940.
The Draining of the Fens, 1944.
R. F. MCNEILE, *Christianity in Southern Fenland*, 1948.
K. R. MACKENZIE, *The English Parliament* (Penguin Books), 1950.
B. H. M. VLEKKE, *Evolution of the Dutch Nation*, New York, 1945.

J. VAN VEEN, *Dredge, Drain, Reclaim, The Art of a Nation*, The Hague, 1948.
A. HOLLESTELLE, *Geschied en Waterstaatkundige beschrijving van de Waterschappen en Polders in het Eiland Tholen*, Tholen, 1919.
P. J. MEERTENS, *Letterkundig Leven in Zeeland in de zestiende en de eerste helft der zeventiende Eeuw*, Amsterdam, 1943.
S. J. FOCKEMA ANDREAE, *Studien ober Waterschapgeschiednis*, Leiden, 1950.
Waterschaps organisatie in Nederland en in den Vreemde, Amsterdam, 1951.

(C). PAMPHLETS AND REPORTS

SIR CORNELIUS VERMUYDEN, *Discourse Touching the Draining of the Great Fennes*, 1642.
W. ELSTOBB, *Observations on an Address to the Public*, 1776.
C. LABELYE, *The Result of a View of the Great Level of the Fens*, 1745.
Report of Admiralty Enquiry, Norfolk Estuary Bill, 1849.
J. RENNIE, *Report and Estimate on the Improvement of the Drainage and Navigation of the South and Middle Levels*, 1810.

APPENDIX

Note on the authenticity of the Vermuyden portrait.

THE portrait reputed to be that of Sir Cornelius Vermuyden, attributed to the artist van Miereveld, and reproduced as the frontispiece to this book originally formed part of a large collection of seventeenth century portraits in the possession of Col. Maurice Noel's family for several centuries. Anna Margaretta Vernatti, to whom reference has been made on p. 57, was born in 1684, the only child of Constantine Vernatti, a nephew of Sir Philibert Vernatti, and married Francis Edwards, of Welham Grove, Leicestershire, by whom she had one child, Mary Edwards. Now Mary Edwards married Lord Anne Hamilton, son of the 5th Duke of Hamilton, who assumed on his marriage the name and arms of Edwards. The son of this marriage, Gerard Anne Edwards, married Lady Jane Noel, daughter of the 4th Earl of Gainsborough, and the son of this marriage, Gerard Noel Edwards, eventually succeeded to the estates of his uncle, Henry, 6th Earl of Gainsborough, and then assumed the name of Noel instead of Edwards. That, very breifly, describes the link between the families of Vernatti and Noel.

A list of thirty-one of the portraits then in the possession of the present Col. Noel's father, Col. W. F. N. Noel, of the Great House, North Nibley, Glos., was given in an article on the Vernatti family in *Fenland Notes and Queries*, Vol. VI, pp. 31, 32, 1906, where No. 7 on the list was described as 'Sir Cornelius Vermuyden', and attached to the back of this portrait is still the label in the handwriting of Col. W. F. N. Noel giving the same description. The present writer has been informed by Col. Maurice Noel that the portrait certainly once bore the signature 'M' in one corner although this is no longer visible, and as art experts have expressed the opinion that the treatment certainly indicates an origin from the van Miereveld School, there has always been an acceptance of the identity of the sitter as Vermuyden and of the artist as van Miereveld.

Recently, however, there has come to light the existence in Holland of an almost identical portrait in the possession of the family of van Kretschmar, van Veen, at the Hague, descendants of the Vernatti family through the marriage of Susannah Vernatti, grand-daughter of Sir Philibert Vernatti, to an ancestor eight generations back, Johan Christian von Kretschmar und Flämischdorf. But the main point is that the van Kretschmar portrait has always been considered to be that of Sir Philibert Vernatti, and not of Sir Cornelius Vermuyden.

The life story of Sir Philibert Vernatti, apart from his connection with the Fen drainage, is fairly well documented, if, perhaps, there are in it some conflicting and indeterminate periods. But more or less certain it is that Philibert and his brother Gabriel were in Venice in 1617, and that in October of that year Philibert was created a knight of San Marco. In the following year the two were in Naples where they were imprisoned as suspected spies by the Count of Orsuna, being eventually released through the intervention of a Flemish mistress of the Count. The important feature here in relation to the portrait is that during the period of imprisonment the brothers were confined 'in a tower situated in the middle of a lake', and that Philibert was for some reason so affected by his incarceration that his 'haer van nature pickswart so witt als een swaen geworden was'. In other words, his hair which naturally was as black as pitch became as white as a swan.

Now the portrait from the Noel collection certainly shows a man with greying hair, as will be seen from the reproduction in this book, but by no stretch of imagination could that hair be described as 'so witt als een swaen'. Furthermore, the beard and moustache are brown in colour. In other words, the portrait is not that of a man whose hair was ever 'pickswart', or black as pitch.

It has been said above that the van Kretschmar portrait is almost identical. The main, and only, difference lies in the fact that in the top right-hand corner is a reproduction of a coat of arms consisting, apparently, of part of the Vernatti arms impaled with those of some other family. The Vernatti arms were 'Or, on a mount in base three oak trees proper, on a chief azure an estoile', and in the British Museum, Sloane MSS, is an album which belonged to Sir Philibert Vernatti on the frontispiece of which he himself has emblazoned those arms, as also the arms of other families with which, presumably, the Vernattis intermarried. But none of these latter corresponds exactly to the arms with which the Vernatti arms are impaled on the van Kretschmar portrait. There is, indeed, evidence to show that the arms on this portrait (only about half the Vernatti arms appearing) were added later, as it is known that part of the panel on which the portrait was painted was broken off, a new piece with the incomplete arms being attached.

Heer F. van Kretschmar states that the chain and order which the sitter wears in the two portraits is the order of San Marco and San Lazaro of Venice. If this is so then this might be considered as conclusive evidence to identify the sitter as Sir Philibert Vernatti who, as we know, was created a knight of the order of San Marco, an order in which, as far as we know, Sir Cornelius Vermuyden never had any interest.

At the moment, therefore, there seems to be evidence both for Vermuyden and Vernatti, although it must be pointed out that Col. W. F. N. Noel possessed another portrait which was confidently named as that of Sir Philibert. This was illustrated in the article in *Fenland Notes and Queries* referred to above but has since disappeared. The present situation is that the Noel family have always traditionally accepted the portrait reproduced in this book as that of Vermuyden, while the van Kretschmar family have traditionally accepted it as that of Vernatti, while both families consider their particular portrait to be the original. Until there has been time for a fuller investigation it would be rash to attempt to make any definite pronouncement, and it would certainly be impolitic at this stage for the writer to give any indication of the direction of his sympathies, even if this may be conjectured.

INDEX